Metal Working
Series Book #4

The Milling Machine

Written & Illustrated
By
DAVID J. GINGERY

Printed in U. S. A.

Library of Congress Catalog
Card Number 80-66142

ISBN 978-1-878087-03-4

David J. Gingery Publishing, LLC
P.O. Box 523
Kimberling City, MO 65686

http://www.gingerybookstore.com
Email: sales@gingerybookstore.com

CONTENTS

FOREWORD

If you have followed the series to date, you may have already built a compact home foundry, a small lathe, and a metal shaper. These items of equipment will be a great aid in building the milling machine, and you have learned to master many technical problems, so the construction of this machine will not be so difficult.

This is meant to be a progressive series, because it is not likely that you would assign yourself to some of these exercises merely to acquire skill and knowledge. With the vision of a valuable piece of shop equipment before you, you should have all the motivation you need to spur you on.

Like the lathe and the shaper, this machine is much larger than I first thought possible. It has features that are especially suited for the home shop, and a capacity that is greater than small machines that are offered at popular home shop prices. It is extremely rigid, and early test operations have produced exceptionally fine work.

Like the lathe and the shaper, it performs some of the machine work on its own parts, but we rely heavily on the lathe for most of the machine work. The shaper can be very helpful in planing the flat surfaces and forming the box slides, but of course this work can still be done by hand if you have chosen not to build a shaper.

If you have not yet begun building your shop, I hope you will start soon. This work really is within the ability of an amateur, and you will not be an amateur for long when you have acquired these simple skills.

While I strive to offer enough information on each part of the machine, a certain amount of knowledge is assumed. It can be a great help to do some supplementary reading in other manuals on lathe operation, shaper operation, casting and pattern making, and general shop practice.

Much of the discussion in the first chapter is as a result of problems that readers have told me about in their calls and letters. I very much appreciated this feedback, it has helped me do a better job.

INTRODUCTION

A milling machine applies a rotating tool to the work, while a lathe applies the tool to rotating work. Much of the work that is done on a miller is like that done on a shaper, but the miller is much faster.

Like other machine tools, the modern miller has evolved from a simple beginning. The plano-miller evolved from the shaper, and its main job was to plane large surfaces and cut keyways in heavy shafting. It was much faster than a planer or shaper, but not as versatile as modern machines.

Milling machines are built in a number of styles, and the main differences are in the relative position of the spindle and work table. Generally, it will be either a vertical or horizontal machine, and it will be either plain or universal.

A horizontal miller has its spindle mounted horizontally, and the feed motion of the table is at right angles to the spindle and on a horizontal plane. The spindle is mounted in a column, like the shaper, and the work table is mounted on a knee that slides on vertical ways. It will have limited motion in line with the spindle.

If the main feed motion is fixed at right angles to the spindle, it is called a plain miller. Universal millers have a feed motion that can be at oblique angles to the spindle center, and they have feed mechanisms that generate compound motions of the table and work piece.

Vertical mills have the same table motions in each class, but the spindle is mounted vertically in a quill.

The engraving on the following page is of a number 8 Brainard plain milling machine. It was massively built in all of its parts. The spindle was 2⅛" in diameter, and it could be raised 6½" above the table. The table was 6" wide and 24" long. It had an automatic feed of 10½". The cross motion in line with the spindle was 4⅜". Notice the huge diameter of the over arm, and the broad face of the spindle gear. This was a heavy duty machine, able to make a very deep cut in a single pass. It weighed 950 pounds, and sold for $275.00 in 1888.

We've borrowed the main features of this machine in this project, and we replaced the over arm with a tail stand to adapt it for home construction and use.

The Brainard Number 8 Plain Milling Machine

The engravings on the facing page show how advanced the machines were in 1888. These models could do most of the jobs that modern machines do.

The specifications and engravings are from an 1888 Hill and Clarke machinery catalog.

	No. 1.	No. 2.
Automatic longitudinal feed	36 in.	24 in.
Vertical range below spindle	24 "	21 "
Cross motion in line with spindle	8 "	7 "
Number of speeds for driving belt	6	6
Width of driving belt	4 in.	3½ in.
Number of changes for feed	4	4
Size of cutter that can be used under arm . .	12 in.	10 in.
Will mill out from column	18 "	16 "
Weight, complete, boxed for shipment . .	4,800 lbs.	3,500 lbs.
Price, with countershaft, no attachments . .	$850	$650
Price, complete, with regular attachments . .	$1,180	$980
Speed of countershaft.	100 rev.	120 rev.
Diameter tight and loose pulleys	14 in.	14 in.
Width tight and loose pulleys	4½ "	4 "

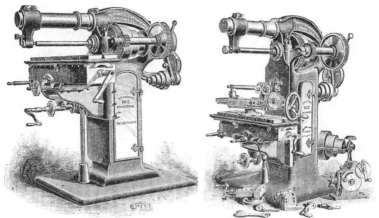

No. 1 Universal Milling Machine.   No. 2 Universal Milling Machine.
With attachments.

While we could have built the miller on a column, it is certain that it would have been difficult to achieve proper alignment of all of the parts. Notice how massive the over arms are on the machines above, and how complex it would be to bore the spindle saddle and the over arm support.

The type of machine we are building was called a Lincoln type milling machine at the turn of the century. It is the lathe type of bed that distinguishes it from the column type construction shown above. These machines were designed for production work, and they were popular because they were so easy to set up and operate. It did not require a highly skilled machinist to operate them.

There were a few vertical mills around at the turn of the century, but they did not become common for some time. The earliest ones were universal machines like those above, and they were fitted with a right angle geared adapter for jobs that required a vertical spindle. We can do nearly as well by fitting the work table with a right angle plate, so we have most of the advantages of both designs.

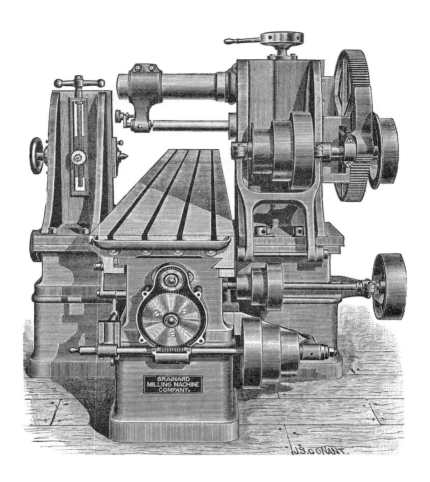

This is Brainard's 84 inch milling machine, another example of the Lincoln type. Notice that it has both an over arm and a tail stand. The over arm was 5" in diameter at the smallest part, and it was solid steel. The spindle was 4" in diameter, and the cutter arbor was 2½". Typical speed ranges of these machines were 8 RPM to 50 RPM.

The table was 84 inches long and 20 inches wide. It had an automatic feed of 7 feet. It weighed 7,500 pounds, and sold for $1,200.00 in 1888.

How would you like to hand scrape the bed and slides on this big fellow? That's the way they did it in 1888!

The design presented in this manual is a miniature of the classic Lincoln type. It is especially suited for home construction, because the lathe type bed makes it easy to do an accurate job of boring the spindle saddle. When it is complete you will have the means to build a column type or a vertical type, but I think you will find that neither is as valuable for the home shop as this simple design.

There have been a large number of small horizontal type millers built, but most had a lathe like head stock, and the carriage was fitted with a vertical slide. They were really lathes with a milling attachment, and were difficult to set up. By making the spindle head adjustable vertically, and the work table rigid, set up is easier and the work is more firmly supported.

When you add a right angle plate, or an adjustable angle plate, you have the same capability as a vertical mill, and both the work and the tool have better support.

If you study the specifications of the small machines on the market, you will see that few of them have a spindle speed range that is below 300 RPM. This is simply too fast for a large share of the work. You will soon see the value of the lower speed range in this machine.

The design of the transmission is of particular importance because of the vertical travel of the spindle head. It was a tough problem to solve, but the solution was simple. In addition to maintaining even belt tension throughout the vertical travel of the spindle, it removes the greater part of the motor weight from the spindle head. There is no tension between the bench and the spindle head because the motor is suspended from the floating rail.

The ability to make your own cutters and holders is as important as being able to build the machine, and the lathe like features are a great help in this as well as making a tapered arbor, or boring the spindle chuck.

There are a large number of lathe operations, and much of the work can be done on the shaper if you have built one, but there is still a lot of hand work. You will be relieved of much of the hand work on future projects when the miller is complete.

This is a progressive series of projects, and there is somewhat more detail in the miller than there was in the lathe or the shaper, but the basic methods are the same. I will spend some time discussing the methods in case you have not built the lathe or the shaper, and hopefully to answer some questions that have been asked by readers to date. The suggestions for each operation are merely samples, and there is more than one way to do most jobs. Much of this simple know how has been forgotten, and it is a real thrill to rediscover it as you work out the construction problems. It is not likely that most of us will ever be able to afford a full array of commercially built machines, tools, and accessories, so we will have to bend our backs and skin our knuckles if we ever hope to have a shop. These simple methods can be the answer

CHAPTER I
CONSTRUCTION METHODS

HAND WORK

Even though this project depends heavily on the lathe, and possibly the shaper, there is still a great deal of hand work. Hacksawing, filing, hand scraping, drilling, and tapping make up a large part of the job. Such work can be tedious, and it could completely discourage you if it is not done right. Given the right tool, and using the proper technique, these chores can become almost enjoyable. "Almost", I say, because you may learn to enjoy it, but I must admit that I don't. I won't promise to make it a pleasure, but I may be able to reduce the misery a little bit.

HACKSAWING

Select the right blade, mount it properly in a rigid frame, and make full length strokes at the rate of 60 per minute or less. You need a sturdy bench vise for sawing, and for most of the hand work in this project. Lift the blade slightly on the back stroke for longer blade life.

Saw blades come in either flexible or rigid, and there is a specific purpose for each. A rigid blade is sometimes called all "hard". They cut more accurately, but they break easily. Flexible blades are of special alloy, and only the tooth portion is tool hard. They cut close enough for these projects, and they will stand a lot of abuse. Those that are generally available have 18, 24, or 32 teeth per inch. Fine tooth blades are for thin material, and coarse ones are for heavy material. If you tackle a 1¼" riser with an 18 tooth blade it will be a breeze, but you may well give up in discouragement if you try it with a 32 tooth blade.

There are "bargain" blades on the market, but they can usually be rated as scrap. You can't build your machines with that kind of "scrap", so choose what you buy with a lot of care. One 18 tooth and one 24 tooth blade in flexible high speed steel will likely last through the entire project, and still be good when you are finished.

FILING

Aluminum is difficult to file because it tends to clog up the teeth. You can reduce the problem by rubbing the teeth with a piece of chalk, but you will need to pick out stubborn chips with a sharp punch or scriber from time to time.

A double cut file will remove material much faster than a single cut, and it does not clog up as easily. A single cut file can be used for the final finish when you are near dimension.

Filing is much like hacksawing, the cut is made on the forward stroke, and you lift slightly on the back stroke. Pace your strokes much slower than for hacksawing.

Draw filing is done by drawing the file sideways along the work. It makes a smoother and more accurate cut, and it is the right way to true up the edges of the steel ways.

A premium file is well worth the extra cost.

HAND SCRAPING

We've lived in the machine age for so long now that we have forgotten many of the fundamental skills. As recently as 40 years ago, nearly every grease monkey knew how to fit a bearing or a cylinder head by hand scraping. It's regarded as a "lost art" now, but it's a simple process.

A test standard is selected that represents the desired finish. If you want to produce a flat surface, a true flat test standard is used. If you want to fit a bearing to the journal, the journal itself can be the standard, or a shaft that has the same dimension and finish as the journal can be prepared. It's not so difficult to come up with an accurate round test standard, but a flat surface is another matter.

Commercially, a surface plate is used for flat work, and if you have a surface plate you can use it to produce another one. Few of us have a surface plate, and we're not likely to persuade anyone to lend us one, so we have to originate one from what is at hand. In book 3 I described a surface plate that was made from plates of glass mounted in a bed of body putty. This actually worked very well, but I left mine in the sun and the wooden base warped, cracking the glass. I think it better to leave the glass unmounted, unless you care to make a base of cast aluminum for mounting the glass.

I specify plate glass because its natural finish is more accurate than sheet glass. It will require much less work. If you support the plate uniformly, coat it with valve grinding compound, and rub another plate over its surface, both plates will be ground until their surfaces are alike. It's a simple process, and it doesn't take very long. The result depends on the care you use in evenly distributing pressure, and rotating the work to ensure even grinding all over. As plate glass is very near true flat as manufactured, you can produce a pair of very accurate plates in this way.

The old method for originating a straight edge or plane surface depended on what was known as "the rule of three". It is possible that you can have an error even though two apparently flat surfaces match, because one can be concave, and the other can be convex. But, if three surfaces can be matched interchangeably, there can be no error. The plates were made of cast iron, and some were so large that a crane was used to move them about. They were allowed to season outdoors for as long as six months or a year before they were planed. Enough material was planed from the surface to remove any strains so they would not warp. They were numbered in sets of three, and the work began. Number one would be scraped to fit numbers two and three, then two and three were scraped to fit each other. Then three and one, and so forth until they would match interchangeably. This was the same method that was used to originate a straight edge, and it's not nearly as tedious as you may imagine.

The work is stained with a test color, and I have found nothing better than Prussian blue oil paint that is used by artists that don't practice the "art" of hand scraping. You just wipe it on with a soft cloth to stain the work uniformly, and it dries in moments. When you rub the work on the test standard, the color will be rubbed off the highest spots, and you will know where to scrape.

Aluminum is very easy to scrape, and you can use ordinary wood working chisels that are honed to a very sharp edge. Or, MSC® Industrial Supply has three cornered scrapers available for purchase. You can contact them by phone at 1-800-645-7270 or view their catalog on the web at www.mscdirect.com/. You can also make scrapers out of old files, but you must grind them very flat, and hone the edges to razor sharpness.

Only a small amount of material is removed after each test, and the entire surface is blued before you test again.

Of course you can't rub the surfaces of the box slides on the surface plate, so we scrape the mounting pads for the ways, and the mounted ways become the test standard for the box slides.

You can produce a reasonably flat surface by planing on the shaper, facing off, or milling, but it will still need an amount of hand scraping to bring it true flat.

It may take an hour or two of practice on a piece of scrap, but it is one of the most valuable skills you can acquire for the home shop operation.

In order to make a reliable test of the surface, the work must rest on the surface plate without wobble. Naturally you would have a false indication if you test on more than one plane, and you would not know where to scrape. It is necessary to prepare the work for scraping by machining, filing, rough scraping, or grinding. You can lay a sheet of abrasive cloth or waterproof sand paper on the surface plate, or other test standard, and use it to grind down any high spots until the work will rest firmly on the standard.

The finished box slides furnish the test standard if the ways need to be scraped parallel, and any mating part can be used as a test standard if it is finished true.

Don't attempt to lap the aluminum slides by rubbing them with the ways coated with grinding compound. The aluminum is the softer metal, and the abrasive grains will embed in it. The steel ways will quickly be ruined.

DRILLING

All of my drilling in these projects to date has been done with an electric hand drill, so I think it fair to call this hand work.

The main problem with using a hand drill is to get the hole at right angles to the surface. Like other hand operations, it takes a little practice. It's much like learning to shoot a pistol from the hip, or throwing a rock at a tin can. There is no science to it, but you have the skill if you let yourself discover it. Practice drilling in some scrap, and criticise your results. It won't be long before you become good at it.

I've added a drill guide to my shop, but only to acquire the spindle for the milling machines quill support. There are a number of them on the market now. "Portalign", Black & Decker's "Drill Guide", etc. have a ⅝" spindle that is about 12" long. It has a ⅜-24 male thread on one end, and the other end has a female thread. It's used to extend the chuck for use in the guide, and it works very nicely in the millers quill support.

Twist drills are sold in varying grades, and there are some "bargains" around. If it is not a U.S. made high speed steel drill, it is probably worthless for the purpose of this project. Carbon steel bits are used for drilling in wood and soft metals, and high speed bits are used for machine work. A high speed drill will cost more, but it is likely to last a lifetime unless you break it.

For this project you will need ⅛", ¹³⁄₆₄", ¼", ⁵⁄₁₆", and ⅜" drills. You are likely to break a ⅛" bit from time to time, so it's a good idea to have some spares.

Step drilling means to begin with a small pilot hole and enlarge it with progressively larger bits. It makes the job easier, and holds the hole closer to its intended center. A typical job will be to install a ¼" screw, so you punch the center, drill a ⅛" pilot hole through both members, enlarge the hole to ¹³⁄₆₄", and enlarge the hole in the outside member to ¼". The inside hole is tapped through the outside hole to ensure alignment.

On those members that are joined by a row of screws, you should complete one hole and install the screw before you do the remaining holes. This is a bit tedious, but there is no other way to achieve alignment without exotic equipment. The slide clamps and ways are an example.

TAPPING

Taps and dies are also available in carbon or high speed steel. All of the threading is done by hand at low speed, so carbon steel taps and dies will be durable enough if you use a quality brand. It's nice to have a full set in a fitted case, but you only need taps in #8-32, #10-24, ¼-20, ⁵⁄₁₆-18, and ⅜-16. It's true that you could buy a full set of cheap imported taps and dies for the price of these sizes individually, but they would prove a disappointment. Most of the tapped holes can be drilled clear through, but a few locations will require tapping blind holes. This is a touchy business because the chips will fill the hole and bind the tap. Always clear the hole of drill chips before you begin to tap, and make sure the hole is deep enough for clearance at the bottom.

The two main causes of broken taps are binding from the chips and starting the tap at an angle. By using the bolt hole in the outside member as a guide for the tap, you will be assured of reasonable alignment. If you advance the tap in fractional turns, and back it up from time to time, the chips will fall clear and rest in the bottom of the hole to be blown out later, or they will fall out in the case of a hole that is drilled clear through. A tap can bind up as you withdraw it too, so be gentle. If it binds at any time, just work it back and forth until it is free.

THE METAL SHAPER

I hand scraped the top of the milling machine bed and installed the steel ways before I mounted it on the shaper to plane off the bottom surface. Only the ends need to be planed so they mate well with the mounting bases, but I did the entire bottom. I used the miller's temporary work table as an auxiliary table on the shaper, but later realized I could have merely tapped holes in the millers bed ways to mount it on the shapers table.

Many of the flat surfaces can be faced off on the lathe much easier than they can be planed on the shaper, and all of them can be finished by hand if you have not built the shaper. It can be a real help on some of the parts, but you don't need a shaper to build the miller.

I cast a simple aluminum channel and fitted it with set screws to serve as a vise for many of the small jobs.

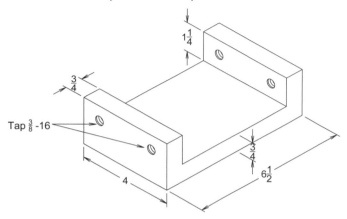

It's a simple pattern and casting job, and when it is planed off on the bottom and finished on the inside, it is a good fixture for clamping the box slides for shaping.

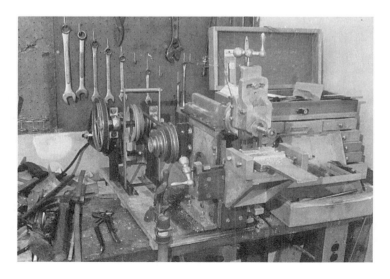

Some items, such as the mounting bases, were just bolted to the shaper table and planed off top and bottom. Use the normal construction holes when you can, or tap holes in areas that won't interfere later.

In the photo below, I've used one of the holes in the tail stand base, and clamped a stop on the table to avoid a hole that would weaken the base. The top surface was planed first, then the wear pads were planed parallel. The shaper is making a .060" cut to bring the clamp pads to ¼" depth. It required only a few minutes of hand scraping to bring it to a good fit, so this operation saved a lot of time.

LATHE WORK

There are a large number of parts that require machining on the lathe. We'll cover the construction of chucks and other accessories in book 6, but I hope to persuade you that a simple metal lathe with a face plate and centers is sufficient to do the work required for this project.

If you are not experienced in lathe work, order a copy of "South Bend's" "How To Run A Lathe" from Lindsay Publications, PO Box 538, Bradley, Ill., 60915, or study another good manual of operation.

TURNING

Such parts as the feed screw arbors and the spindle are simply mounted between centers and driven by a dog for turning them to shape and size.

FACING OFF

You can face off anything that can be bolted to the face plate, so long as it will swing clear of the bed.

Some items require spacers to hold them away from the face plate for boring clearance, but others can be bolted in place through the face plate slots. Ordinary set screw collars make very handy furniture for spacing for many set ups.

The photo below shows the universal base being faced off. The back side has already been faced off, the center hole is bored to .625", the ⅜" wide slot has been machined, and the outside diameter has been reduced. The only accessory was a pair of ⁵⁄₁₆" x 1" bolts that enter tapped holes in the casting through the face plate slots.

DRILLING AND BORING IN THE LATHE

In order to bore a true hole you need a starting hole. I use a Morse taper shank adapter and a ½" hand tighten chuck mounted in the tail stock quill for drilling work on the face plate.

If you face off a cone shaped starting dimple in the work, the drill will enter and cut very true. Hold the shank of the adapter with a vise grip pliers, and advance the drill with the tail stock screw.

In the photo below I'm drilling the starting hole for the ⅝" bore in the universal base. The set screw collar on the drill is to prevent drilling through the casting and into the head stock spindle socket.

The drilled hole is not accurate enough, and it must be bored to its final size with a forged boring tool on the tool post. Many jobs will require boring to fit a mandrel, and additional operations will be performed when it is mounted on the mandrel between centers. This is so all work will be concentric with the original center. It's not difficult if you follow the right procedure.

In the photo below the universal base is being bored to .625" with the forged boring tool. The black tape is a depth gauge to signal the end of each pass.

BORING TOOLS

You can order light forged boring tools from most tool catalogs, but they are easy to make. You'll need several styles if you do much shop work.

Buy a 36" length of ¼" drill rod from the industrial supply house, and you can make as many as 8 tools for the price of one.

The usual style is made by heating the end of the rod to a bright red, and forging a short hook on the end. It is hardened and tempered, and the end is ground to shape.

You'll need what is termed a "D" style tool for the many small bores in this project. The end profile looks like a "D", and it will enter a smaller starting hole than the usual hook style.

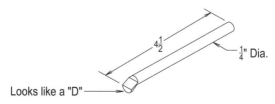

$4\frac{1}{2}$"

$\frac{1}{4}$" Dia.

Looks like a "D"

Just heat the end to a bright red, and swell it with a few blows of the hammer. The main object is to swell it on the left side as it enters the hole. The right side should be about parallel with the shank of the tool, and so should the bottom. The flat plane on the top should be above the center line of the tool when it is ground.

It is hardened by heating to a bright red and quenching quickly. Ask, when you buy your rod, whether it should be quenched in oil or water. Don't harden the entire tool, only the working end.

It will be too brittle if left fully hardened, so you must temper it. Polish the hardened end with emery cloth, and reheat it until it turns a straw color, then quench it.

Now, you may not be the village smithy, but you can at least forge your own simple boring tools.

ACCURACY IN BORING

These light tools tend to spring away from the work, and it takes special technique to make a predictable cut. It is not at all difficult if you know how.

A typical job will be to enlarge a ⅜" starting hole to exactly .500"or .625". This may seem impossible without a very accurately graduated dial on the cross feed screw, but the dial would be of little value for this job, even if you had one.

As the cutting edge of the tool is drawn against the inside of the hole it will spring away. The deeper the cut, the greater the tendency to spring away. The depth that is indicated by the graduated dial is not true. This seems to pose a serious problem, but you can easily find the amount of yield by a series of trial cuts, and it will be uniform so long as the tool remains clamped in the test position.

Let's say you set the depth of cut at .025". It will probably remove about .015" on the first pass, about .006" on the second pass, maybe .003" or .004" on the third pass, and about .001" on the fourth pass. A fifth pass may remove an additional .001", or it may just brush the surface. You must make as many passes as are needed to clean up the bore without changing the depth of the tool. You measure the size of the hole after each pass, and compare it with its original size. After you have made comparisons, you will know how deep you can cut without taking the yield of the tool into consideration, and you can calculate how many rough passes you can make before you have to begin a more precise series of cuts

This set of ratios must be determined for each new set up. The size and length of the tool will determine its flexibility; and the nature of the material, the cutting speed, and the feed rate will have an effect. You will quickly be able to evaluate all these factors.

You can take cuts as deep as .050" in the early stages of boring the hole, but make multiple passes on each setting, and learn the effect of each pass. When you near finished size, you must take only very light cuts.

CALCULATING CUTTING DEPTH

If you are using the home made lathe, or any other lathe that does not have a graduated feed dial on the cross feed, it is a simple matter to calculate the depth of cut.

The cross feed screw on the home made lathe is a ¼-20 screw. That means that there are 20 threads per inch, so the cross feed will advance ¹⁄₂₀" for each full turn of the screw. Converted to a decimal, that is .050" (Divide one by twenty). Since the tool movement is on the radius of the circle, you will effect the diameter by twice as much as the setting. If you move the tool .050", the diameter will be changed by .100". A half turn of the screw will be a cut of .050", and a quarter turn will be .025". Any other fraction of a turn is easily calculated, and you will soon be able to finish within .001" of the planned size. I plan my work so that the end of each series of boring cuts will end on even multiples of .025". In that way, when I know that I have reached a diameter of .600", I know that one more set of passes will finish up at .625" if I advance the cut exactly ¼ turn of the screw, or .0125".

If you have any other lathe, you can easily count the number of turns that travel the cross slide one inch. That will give you the screw pitch, and you can work it out by the same method. If it takes 8 turns of the screw to travel one inch, then each turn is ⅛", or .125".

Of course you can easily add a graduated collar by the simple methods that we will discuss a bit later. There is an error built into every machine, and you must learn to compensate for it in your setting up. A graduated collar is only an aid, and its indication means nothing unless you are comparing it with the previous cut.

SIMPLE LATHE ACCESSORIES

As you get more deeply involved in machine work, accessories become more desirable. They are very expensive, and it's difficult to justify their cost in the home shop.

Three jaw chucks have special appeal because they are self centering. This is a real convenience for simple round work, but you will soon find that most of your work will require mounting off center.

A four jaw chuck is the more practical item if you can only afford one chuck, because it can hold both centered and offset work.

Neither type is a necessity in the home shop, because they are really conveniences that can well be done without. As you perform the operations in this manual, you will see that a commercially made chuck would be of little value for this project.

A SET SCREW CHUCK

These simple fixtures are easy to make, and they will do any job that would normally call for a three or four jaw chuck. They can be made to bolt on the face plate, or you can cast them with a hub, and bore it to fit the spindle in place of the face plate.

The smaller size will handle all centered work up to 1" in diameter. You can use a series of split pulley bushings to mount work smaller than or you can make a bushing for any particular job that is not standard size.

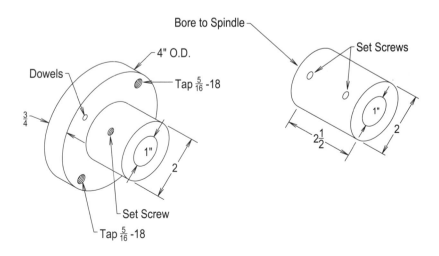

The chuck on the previous page is made to mount on the face plate with two ⁵⁄₁₆-18 cap screws through the face plate slots. A pair of close fitting dowel pins will return it to its proper center each time you install it on the plate. The hub portion need extend only about 1½", and you can bore it after it is faced off on the back side and mounted on the face plate with the dowels installed.

This is the sort of fixture you would use if you were going to make your own flanged sleeve bearings for the milling machines spindle head.

It's a simple pattern, and a simple casting. Feed it with a 1¼" sprue at the rim, and set a 1¼" riser in the center.

The chuck detailed below is merely a simpler version that is meant to mount on the spindle nose.

Some of the work, such as the feed screw handles, will require a larger fixture. These are sometimes called a bell chuck or a ring chuck. It's the same idea, but they are larger. They are fit with four set screws in the rim, so you can clamp work that is smaller than the inside diameter of the chuck, and you can adjust it to center. They can be made to bolt to the face plate, or you can make it with a hub to fit the spindle nose.

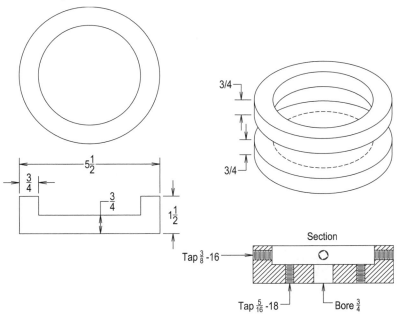

The pattern is a simple matter, being just a ring and a disc of ¾" pine stock. You can mount it on the face plate to true it up. Of course it needs a little draft both inside and out. It's rammed into the drag, and you need to vent generously so gas won't be trapped in the inverted cup. Feed with a 1¼" sprue at the rim, and set a 1¼" riser in the center.

The ⁵⁄₁₆" tapped holes in the back are for mounting it on the face plate. You can use these holes to mount it for facing off the back side, then invert it to machine the inside of the rim and face off the bottom of the cup. The four holes in the rim are tapped for the set screws. They should slant towards the back a tiny amount, so work will be forced against the bottom of the cup, and the centers of the screws should meet in the center of the chuck. The ¾" hole is bored in the center so that you will have clearance to bore through any work that is mounted in the chuck.

The photo below is of the finished chuck being used to drill the ⅜" starting hole in one of the feed screw hand wheels.

Longer screws are used for smaller work. Always rotate the job by hand to make sure the screws clear the bed. Be very careful to avoid getting your clothing tangled in the screws. Never go near a machine tool with a neck tie on, and don't wear loose fitting clothes. I won't even wear a long sleeved shirt in my shop.

The hand wheel is left in the same position in the chuck, and the hole is bored to .500" to fit the screw spindle.

A set screw is then installed in the hub, and the hand wheel is mounted between centers on an arbor to complete the machine work.

MACHINING THE ARBORS

Any work that is bored can be mounted between centers on an arbor, or mandrel, to do turning and facing jobs.

My most useful accessory is the stepped arbor. Each step is 1¼" long, except the ¾" step, which is 2½" long. A flat is ground on each step for the set screw to seat on.

You can make additional straight arbors in each size, and about 8" long, and you will be equipped for any of the jobs in this project.

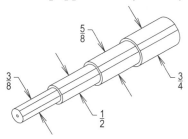

MAKE A FACE PLATE CLAMP

These simple angle plate clamps will handle any of the jobs in the project that would require a four jaw chuck. Once you've made and used them, you'll be glad you didn't blow your bait and beer money on a chuck. We'll get into the construction of chucks in book 6, so save your money for more important things.

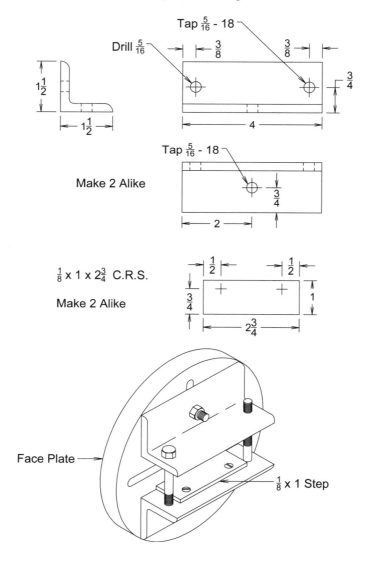

You can use standard structural angle iron, or you can make patterns and cast them in aluminum. A 1½" angle, either ³⁄₁₆" or ¼" thick will work very well. If you do them in aluminum, make them ⅜" thick.

They won't be true square, so they need to be faced off to be accurate. Simply drill and tap them as shown on the drawings. Locate the holes carefully, so that both halves will be identical. Notice that the clamp bolts enter the clamp from opposite ends for balance. When the angles are brought face to face, one hole will be tapped, and the other is drilled.

To true them up, bolt one of the angles to the face plate with a ⁵⁄₁₆" cap screw and flat washer. Test the angle between the leg and the face plate. Slip shims under either edge until the angle is exactly 90 degrees as indicated by an accurate try square.

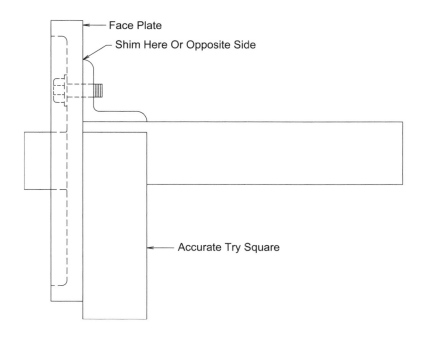

Face Plate

Shim Here Or Opposite Side

Accurate Try Square

Now, bolt the mating angle to the leg of the mounted angle, and face it off on the lathe.

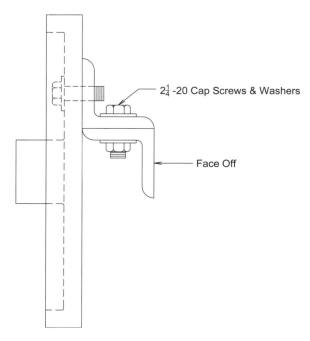

$2\frac{1}{4}$ -20 Cap Screws & Washers

Face Off

Finally, without separating the angles, invert the entire assembly. Mount the faced off leg on the face plate, without the shims, and face off the other leg.

If your face plate is true, and the original set-up was correct, both angles will be exact and the clamping surfaces will be parallel.

The ⅛" x 1" cold rolled flats are fastened to the inside of each angle to provide a step that is parallel to the surface of the face plate. This makes it possible to mount rectangular work so that you can face off two sides parallel. It also makes it possible to clamp rectangular work for accurate boring.

In use, the work is clamped loosely, the tail center is moved up to center it in the clamps, and the clamp bolts are tightened carefully to prevent shifting. Exactly as you do when you use a four jaw chuck. You will soon find dozens of uses for this simple fixture, and you will find ways to use the same principle on the work table of your miller.

FOUNDRY WORK

"THE CHARCOAL FOUNDRY", book 1 in the series, is intended to present the simplest and lowest cost means to melt the aluminum for your castings. It covers only the rudiments of foundry work, and there is a great deal to learn beyond what is presented in those few pages. You have much to gain by reading other manuals on the subject, and I urge you to do it.

As this is a progressive series, I strive to present the important details as the need arises. Many of the parts are especially designed with a scant shop in mind, and they would be done differently if commercial equipment were available to do the machining operations.

I feel that a book of solutions to problems is not worth very much until you are actually facing the problems that are being discussed. With a few basic principles in mind, you can go to work and make castings, and a critical look at the results will teach you more than any book.

FOUNDRY PROBLEMS

True love never runs smoothly, and foundry work is only slightly less fickle. You may be able to send a petulant wife home to her mother, but you will have to live with your foundry problems until you solve them. The problems will have a simple common sense answer, and I urge you to make a mold and pour it, even if you don't fully understand all you are doing. Don't be foolhardy, but proceed with caution, and pay close attention to what is happening. You will learn a great deal from each experience, and that's more fun than reading books.

Provided that you have good sand, every casting will be good if the mold is properly rammed, vented, gated, and the metal is poured at the right temperature. With a few guiding principles, you can evaluate your work and see if you have got it right.

MOLDING SAND

This is the most difficult part to express because there is no way to draw a picture of it, and a photograph wouldn't be any help either. We'll have to use something in our common experience for a comparison.

If you'll open a package of brown sugar, and crumble it up so that the grains are separate, you'll have a good idea of what loose molding sand looks like. Then take a handful of it and squeeze it into a cake. That is about what the tempered sand feels like, except that it is not so sticky. You can squeeze it into a cake, and it will be resilient so that you could compress it even more if you wanted too. It will break in half without crumbling up on you, and it will take the shape of the pattern.

Properly blended sand will have just enough clay in it to coat each grain of sand. Properly tempered sand will have just enough water so that the clay will be plastic.

If there is too much clay the sand won't vent properly, and if there is too much water the mold will generate steam when you pour in the metal.

MOLDING PRACTICE

Molding practice is the main source of trouble, and a part of it relates to the pattern. You can't make a good mold with a bad pattern. Provide ample draft and a smooth surface on your patterns. If you can't withdraw it easily you are certain to damage the mold and there will be sand inclusions in the casting. Wipe a small fillet of body putty on all inside corners, and slightly round all outside corners except at the parting plane. Seal all patterns with two or more coats of varnish, lacquer, or shellac.

We all ram too tightly as beginning molders, but that is not so serious if you remember to vent generously with the wire. I persist in ramming too hard because I'm inclined toward shameful displays of vulgar emotion when a cope drops out when I close up a mold. You are probably more stable, and you can take chances if you want to.

It is more important to ram uniformly, whether too hard or not, because a mold won't be sound if any part of it is very much softer than the rest. Pay extra attention to pockets and corners, and strive for uniform density throughout the entire body of the mold.

Swabbing around the pattern will strengthen the bond at the edge so it is less likely to break when you rap and draw the pattern. Swab the surface of gates and runners, and any corner or edge that looks like it may cause trouble when the mold is poured. Dust the cavity and newly swabbed areas with parting before you close up to pour.

The sprue opening should be funnel shaped at the top, and you should pour directly into it. If you pour to the side, you will wash loose sand into the mold. Swab both the bottom and top of the sprue, and dust the top with parting before you pour.

Blow out the sprue and any risers carefully, and turn the cope horizontal before you swing it over the drag. This will allow any loose particles to fall clear.

Close the mold firmly, but don't jar it. You may knock a portion loose and it will cave in on you. Be careful not to jar the mold when you move it to the pouring area.

The lowest portion of the casting will be the most sound and faithful in detail, except when trapped gas forces the molten metal away from the surface of the cavity. A flaw that is caused by trapped gas will be easy to recognize, and the cure is to use the vent wire more generously before you roll over the drag.

Shrink cavities will normally be at the top of the casting. Sprues and risers must be as large or larger than the thickness of the portion of the mold they serve. If they are too small they will solidify before the casting, and rob metal from the mold to leave a shrink cavity. Gates and runners are made to enter at the heaviest section of the mold, and risers are attached as near as possible to the heavy sections that they serve.

It's a common error to try to make repairs on the parting plane after the cope is rammed. The result is a run out between the flask halves. You can slick up the face of the drag before the cope is rammed up, but don't touch it after the cope is rammed.

If your flasks are not well fastened at the corners they will yield when you try to move them about, and the sand will break loose. A groove or a rib on the inside of the cope will prevent the sand falling out on smaller molds, but you need cross ribs in larger flasks to give the sand body extra support.

I make all of my flasks with a ⅜" groove on the inside, and I've made up several ribs from ¾" stock that have a tongue to fit the grooves of the flasks. You can cut grooves in the ribs too, or you can drive roofing nails into them to give a better grip on the sand.

You can also make up some "gaggers" out of sheet metal. They fit over the ribs like a saddle, to help support the broad expanse of sand.

The dimensions will depend on the size of your flasks, and the problem at hand.

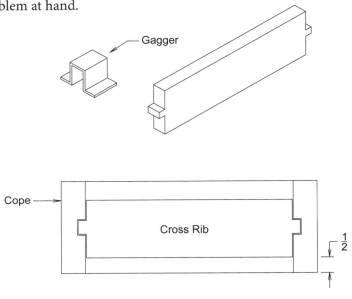

You will certainly need cross ribs on several molds in this project, and you may find it necessary to use gaggers if your sand is not well bonded.

SPLIT PATTERNS

Many of the patterns have draft both above and below the parting line, and they are split for easier molding. They are aligned with small pins made of nails, and these must fit freely enough so the halves will separate when the mold is opened.

Some of them are dual purpose patterns, and one or more parts of them will be used to cast different parts for the milling machine.

None of the patterns are unusually difficult, and hand tools are all you need to make them. A table saw is nice, but there is not so much work that it can't be done with a hand saw.

White pine is the easiest common wood to work with, and it serves very well for pattern making.

MELTING AND POURING

The ideal temperature for pouring aluminum is from 1375 to 1450 degrees Fahrenheit. Those numbers mean very little to you unless you have an accurate pyrometer, and there is no need for you to go to that expense. You can quickly learn how to judge the temperature without a pyrometer.

In general, molds with thin sections need hotter metal than those with heavy sections. Also, larger molds need to be poured a little hotter if the metal has to travel some distance to fill the mold.

The metal will actually be fluid at something near 1200 degrees, but it needs to be super heated so it will remain fluid until the mold is filled. This is the area where you need to develop your judgement. There are sensible characteristics of the melt that you can learn to evaluate. That is: You can evaluate them with your ordinary sense of sight and feel, and you don't need instruments.

As the temperature of the melt increases, it will begin to give off light, and the light will change in color and intensity as the temperature climbs. It first shows a dull red, and gradually brightens through shades of red, orange, yellow, and finally a dazzling white if you approach 2500 degrees Fahrenheit. The shades of color mean something, but only experience can tell you what they mean.

A long time ago, a village blacksmith was trying to teach his worthless son in law how to forge a plow share. He did not want to reveal his secrets, but how else to provide a decent living for his only daughter? He said "you heat it to a bright cherry red, then lay it on the anvil to hammer its point into shape". There was a cherry tree just outside the door, and it was loaded with ripe cherries, so the analogy had clear meaning at the time. I don't know the end of the story, so I can't tell you whether the young man got the thing mastered or not. I do know that "cherry red" does not mean much to me, and I bet it doesn't help you very much either.

One fellow once wrote that "cherry red" was a poor term for comparison and suggested that "incipient redness" was a better expression. I had to look up "incipient", and I'll save you a trip to the dictionary, in case you are as illiterate as I am. It means "in a state of beginning". I don't get much help from that either, because a charge that showed "incipient red" in a dark room, would look like a new dime in bright sunlight. The color of the radiated light means nothing unless all factors have been considered.

The simplest way to judge the temperature is to gently stir the melt with a steel rod about ¼" in diameter. You are feeling for lumps of unmelted stock, and trying to judge the fluidity of the melt. At about 1400 degrees, the molten aluminum will slip easily off the end of the rod. At a lower temperature it will tend to build up a blob that will have to be scraped off. As you feel it, and note its color, you will be making a mental note, and the results of your pour will test your judgement. It will not require more than a half dozen molds and you will have it mastered. It maybe "cherry red", or it may be "incipient red". It's more likely to be "tangerine" in most cases, but pick any fruit you like. Most important, it will be like the porridge of Goldilocks fame: "Not too hot, and not too cold, but just right".

TIPS ON THE CHARCOAL FOUNDRY

The volume and pressure of the air blast is more important than it may seem. If you use a hair drier for an air supply, you are not likely to be troubled with too much air, and a shutter is probably not necessary. If you use a vacuum cleaner, or other more powerful blower, you need to use a shutter to control the blast. Too much air will consume fuel too rapidly, and the flame will be too hot. You can easily burn the bottom out of your pot because of the excess of oxygen. It works like a cutting torch.

You can preheat large chunks of aluminum by building a ring of ordinary bricks around the top of the furnace to hold in the heat. Don't try to melt it, just surround it with bricks, lay a couple of bricks over the top, and heat it to the point of "hot shortness". Then you can easily break it up into smaller pieces with a hammer.

The sludge that forms on the top of the melt has a lot of good aluminum in it. Skim it to the side of the pot, and press it with your skimmer to wring out the good metal. It will turn to a powder when the aluminum has been wrung out, and it will float lightly on the top.

Add fuel frequently as the bed settles. The fire will cool off for a short time if you add a large amount of new fuel. Dump the fuel bed from time to time, to get rid of ashes, then re-fire with the glowing coals and new fuel.

MATERIALS AND SUPPLIES

Wholesale Tool Company, (http://www.wttool.com/) has five large outlets that carry a complete line of machine shop equipment and supplies. They have a complete catalog available on their web site and they accept all major credit cards, and each branch has a toll free ordering number.

Their prices on standard items are very good, and they have many specially priced items.

Wholesale Tool Co. Inc., 12155 Stephens Drive, Box 68, Warren, Michigan, 48090, phone 800-521-3420.

Wholesale Tool Co. Of Oklahoma Inc., 7240 E. 46th St., Box 45952, Tulsa, Oklahoma, 74145, phone 800-331-4075.

Wholesale Tool South Inc., 4200 Barringer Drive, Box 240965, Charlotte, N. C. 28210, phone 800-438-3580.

Wholesale Tool of Indianapolis 601 East Hanna, Indianapolis, Indiana 46227, phone 800-551-2251.

Wholesale Tool of Tampa, Florida 9212 Adamo Drive, Tampa, Florida 33619, phone 800-237-4689

These are not advertisements. None of the companies I list from time to time have paid me to mention them. Most do not even know that I have, but I try to find sources that are likely to respond to the needs of individuals. Nearly all companies have a minimum order amount because of the high cost of filling an order, but it is usually from $15.00 to $25.00, and that is not unrealistic in this age. Some have a highly complex billing system, and they can't process cash orders at all, so I don't list them.

NOW, TO WORK

With the basic methods understood, there is no reason why you can't start building right away. Be especially careful in those areas that are new to you, but don't be intimidated. These are simple skills, and you can do it.

CHAPTER II

BUILDING THE BED

The spindle is horizontal, and its center must be exactly parallel to the bed ways. The completed bed ways will guide the boring bar that bores the spindle head, and all of the various movements of the miller will be established in relation to the bed ways. Like the lathe, the bed is the first order of construction. It's a simple structure, and when it is complete you will be well on the way to owning a milling machine.

THE BED PATTERN

This is a simple shape, and it's not difficult to make if you consider the inside draft before you assemble it.

The pattern will leave four green sand cores in the mold, and it will be tough to withdraw if it is not made right.

All of the sections are 1½" deep, and they taper from ½" thick at the top to ⅜" thick at the bottom.

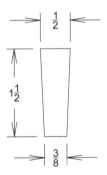

The pattern must be assembled so that it leaves green sand cores that have four sloping sides, and it must be smaller at the top. The sections must be exactly vertical so the pattern won't be locked in the mold.

None of the joints in the pattern will be cut at right angles, but all will be off square by ¹⁄₁₆" so they will mate with the taper of the section sides.

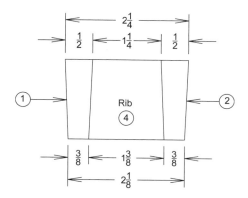

The sectional view of the pattern shows that the rib is ⅛" wider at the bottom, and the pattern is ⅛" wider at the top. The draft is ¹⁄₁₆" in 1½", or ½" per foot. That is much more draft than is needed, but less than that would be difficult to manage without very good wood working machinery and a high level of skill. The excess draft will do no harm, and it makes the job much easier.

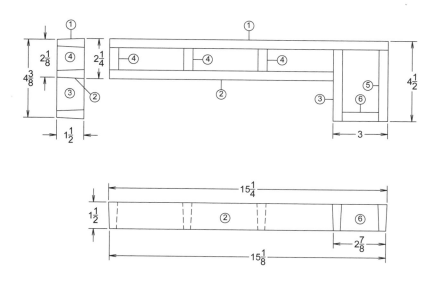

Prepare about 48" of the 1½" tapered stock, and make the end cuts on each piece very carefully. Note that parts 2, 3, and 5 are the same dimension top and bottom, but off square by ¹⁄₁₆". All other parts have equal taper on both ends, and they are ⅛" longer at top or bottom.

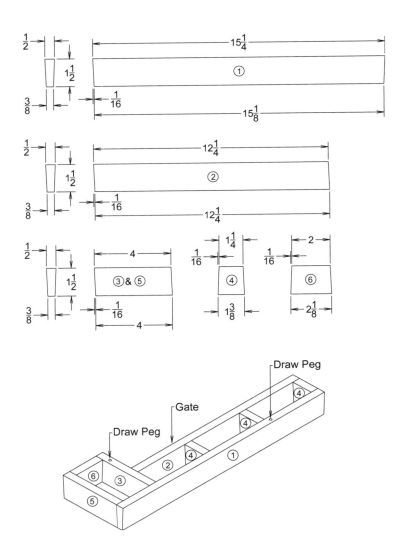

Sand each part smooth, and assemble with glue and brads. Make sure that the top surface is true flat by laying it on the surface plate or other flat surface. This will save a lot of filing and scraping on the casting.

It would be very difficult to sand the inside of the pattern when it is assembled, so make sure all is smooth. Wipe a very small fillet on all inside corners, and slightly round all outside corners except at the top, which is the parting plane. Plastic auto body putty is ideal for forming fillets, and it's great for filling the end grain and any flaws.

Sand the assembled pattern smooth all over, and seal with at least two coats of lacquer, shellac, or varnish. I use clear lacquer in an aerosol can for all of my small patterns.

The spacing between members #4 is not critical, just make it about equal.

Drill two ⅛" holes in the top of the pattern for draw pegs, and note the location of the gate on the sketch.

MOLDING THE BED CASTING

This is not a difficult pattern to mold, but you can have a problem with the green sand cores if you don't ram properly. There is a tendency to ram the cores too hard, and they won't yield when you rap the pattern. They must be as firm as the main body of the drag, so they won't break or crumble at the corners, but don't over do it.

We'll discuss this mold step by step, to review procedure, and the same general principles will apply to all of the molds.

Your flask should measure about 10" x 18" on the inside, and 3" is deep enough for each flask half. You'll need a couple of cross ribs for the cope, a 1¼" sprue pin, and a molding board and a bottom board to fit the flasks.

1. Lay the pattern face down on the molding board, and dust both the board and the pattern with parting. It helps to wipe a new pattern all over with the dust bag when you use it for the first time.

2. Invert the drag over the pattern, and riddle in about 2" of loose sand. Press the sand into the core areas with your fingers, and proceed to peen the sand uniformly all over with the wedge shaped end of the rammer. A moderate force is sufficient, and

don't ram the cores any harder than the rest of the sand. Hold the pattern with your fingers as you ram, so it doesn't move about in the flask.

3. Riddle in another layer of sand, and peen it all over uniformly. Don't bump the pattern with the rammer at any time. Continue to add layers of sand until the drag is mounded full. Then, strike it off level with the bottom of the flask with a straight edge.

It should be well compacted so it will retain the shape of the pattern when it is withdrawn, but not so hard and dense that it won't yield when you rap the pattern. You should be able to press your thumb into the sand with only moderate pressure.

4. Run the vent wire into the sand at about 2" intervals all over the pattern area.

5. Sprinkle some loose sand over the bottom of the drag, rub in the bottom board, and roll over the drag.

8. If the parting face is not clean and smooth, you can slick it up with a trowel. If the sand is not firm at the edge of the pattern or around the sides of the drag, you have not rammed thoroughly or uniformly. It will be best to dump it out and do it over, rather than try to repair the loose areas.

9. Dust the parting face all over, and press a 1¼" sprue pin about ½" into the sand, about 1" away from the edge. Note the gate location on page 40.

10. Set the cope in place, and fit it with a cross rib on each side of the sprue pin. Not all molds will need the ribs, but this one would be very likely to drop out when the mold is opened, or, worse, when it is closed.

11. Riddle in the sand in layers, and ram it with a bit less force than you used for ramming the drag. You don't want to deform the parting face by ramming too hard.

When the cope is mounded full, strike it off level, cut the sprue top to a funnel shape, and rap and withdraw the sprue pin. Run the vent wire in, just as you did for the drag, and smooth up the sprue opening with your fingers. Swab the sprue and dust it with parting before you open the mold. If there are any risers, they get the same treatment as the sprues.

Lift the cope straight up and set it on edge behind the drag.

12. Swab all around the pattern with a soft brush dipped in water, drive a couple of small screws or screw eyes into the draw peg holes, and rap the pattern in all directions. You can rest a screw driver against the peg, and rap its handle with a block of wood. Grasp the draw pegs and lift the pattern straight up in a single motion.

13. Cut the gate from the cavity to the sprue print, and smooth it up with your fingers and by swabbing. Swab the bottom of the sprue opening in the cope, and any part of the mold that threatens trouble. Dust all newly swabbed areas with parting. Use a bright light to look into the cavity, and lift out any loose particles with a lifter or the wet swab.

14. Blow out the sprue with the bellows, turn the cope horizontal to let any loose particles fall clear, and set it gently but firmly in place on the drag.

15. Pour directly into the sprue as rapidly as it will accept the metal, and don't stop pouring until the mold is full.

Because the metal must travel a fair distance to fill the mold, you'll want it to be very hot. Don't forget to skim the pot before you pour.

These are the basic steps for every mold, and I'll point out variations when the need arises. It won't take long before this activity becomes second nature. You can turn out as many as 15 or 20 such castings in a leisurely day once you have mastered it, so it's worth your effort to learn.

FINISHING THE BED CASTING

It would be possible to mount the casting on the shaper table to plane it off, but it is a complicated operation to set up. The job is more easily done by hand on the top surface, and you would need to hand scrape it to the ways even if you planed it off.

Just saw off the gate, and file any drastic high spots until the top surface of the bed will rest on the surface plate without any perceptible wobble.

You can lay a sheet of abrasive cloth or coarse water-proof sand paper face up on the surface plate, and use it to grind down the casting to prepare it for scraping.

Stain the entire top surface of the casting, and rub it back and forth on the abrasive. When all of the stain is ground away, it may look perfect but it is not. It is much faster than scraping, and it saves a lot of time, but this is not true enough for the bed.

Lightly draw file the casting, to remove any grains of abrasive that may be embedded, and stain it all over with the Prussian blue. Clean up the surface plate, and rub the casting over it about ten short strokes. This will show you the high spots, and the serious work begins.

Make sure that the casting rests on the plate without any wobble, or the high spots that are indicated will be false. If necessary, do some rough scraping until there is no wobble. Re-blue the entire surface before each test, and scrape all of the shiny spots equally before you test again.

You can use a three cornered scraper, a wood chisel, a well honed cabinet makers scraper, or anything that can be honed to a very straight and keen edge. A ⅜" square lathe tool bit makes a very effective scraper for steel as well as aluminum.

Continue to test and scrape until you have at least 75% contact over the surface of the bed. You may finish in an hour, or you may spend the rest of today and part of tomorrow, but give it all the time it requires to gain this skill and provide an accurate foundation for your milling machine.

THE MOUNTING BASES

If you have built the metal lathe, these will be old hat to you. They differ only in size.

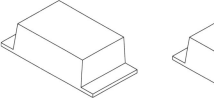 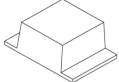

They are of ¼" section thickness throughout, and the patterns have draft both inside and out. While you could use ¼" plywood, white pine is much easier to work with.

Make all parts slope equally on each end, and sand all smooth before assembly.

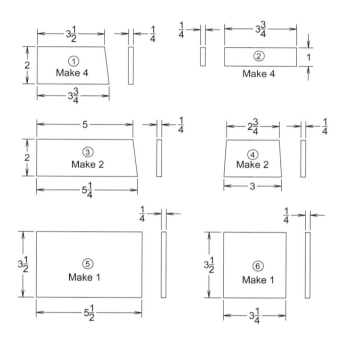

Assembly is just like making a box. It will be best to assemble the sides and ends with glue and brads, then bevel the edge of the feet so they will lay flat and parallel to the bottom, and install them with glue and brads. Install the top panels last of all.

Wipe a small fillet on all inside corners, including the junction at the feet and ends. Fill the end grain and any flaws with body putty, and sand smooth inside and out. The edges of the feet need a slight amount of draft, and round all outside corners except at the parting plane.

Note that the section thickness is not tapered. The inside draft is furnished by the sloping sides and ends.

The larger base is for the left end of the bed, and the smaller one is for the right end.

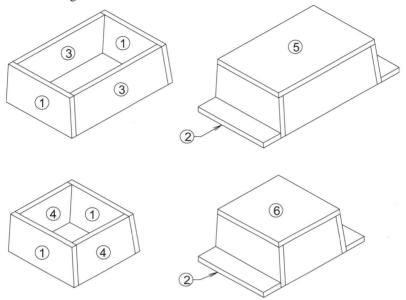

MOLDING THE MOUNTING BASES

This will be a double roll mold so the green sand cores will rest on the face of the drag. We'll actually make the cope first, and you can use the drag half of the flask so the alignment pegs won't interfere.

Set the pattern base down on the molding board, and set a 1" sprue pin in the center of the top, just like a chimney. The sprue will be the pouring gate, and it will provide the means to rap the pattern.

Ram up the cope, just as though it were the drag, strike it off, remove the sprue pin, rub in a bottom board, and roll it over.

Clean up the parting face and the pattern, ram up the drag, vent generously with the wire, rub in a bottom board, and roll over the entire mold. This is the second roll.

Use the sprue pin to rap the pattern before you open the mold, so the pattern will remain on the core.

Cut the sprue to the funnel shape, pull out the pin, and open the mold.

Rap the pattern and lift it from the core, and you are ready to clean up the mold and close it up for pouring.

ASSEMBLING THE BED

An 18 tooth hacksaw blade will easily cut off the sprues, and the top and bottom of the bases need to be trued up. I bolted the bases to the shaper table, and planed them off on both the top and bottom. The same job can be done with a file.

I installed the ways before I planed off the bottom of the bed, and I used the millers temporary work table as an auxiliary table on the shaper. This turned out to be an unreasonable amount of work, and I think it makes more sense to just plane off the bases and file the bottom of the bed.

The object is to fit the bases so that the assembly will rest squarely on the bench without wobble, so the bed won't be twisted when you bolt it in place on the bench.

The bases are bolted to the bed casting with ¼-20 cap screws with flat washers and lock washers. They are centered fore and aft, and they overhang the ends of the bed by about ¾" so the bolt heads will clear the inside of the base.

The bolt locations must be taken from your own assembly. It's best to clamp the base to the bed, locate the hole center, and step drill a ¹³⁄₆₄" tap size hole through the base and about 1" into the bed casting. Enlarge the hole in the base to ¼", and tap the hole in the bed for ¼-20 threads. Be very careful, this is a blind hole. Reassemble the parts with a cap screw, and proceed to do the remaining holes. A bit tedious, but the only way to be sure the holes will be lined up.

The left base is fastened with 4 bolts, and the right base is fastened with 3.

Drill a ⁵⁄₁₆" or ⅜" hole in the center of each foot to complete the bed assembly.

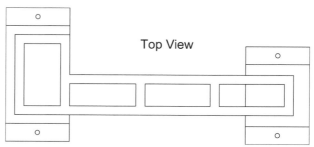

Top View

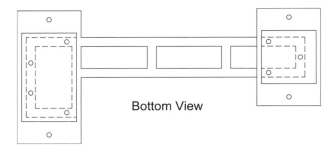

Bottom View

The bottom view shows the approximate bolt locations. There is little room for error because there is only a ⅜ thick webb in the bed casting. Transfer the hole centers very carefully.

THE BED WAYS

This is a slab of ¼" x 3" x 13" cold rolled steel. It is fastened to the bed casting with nine ¼-20 x ¾" flat head screws that are countersunk slightly below the surface. The ways overhang the right end by 1", and by ⁷⁄₁₆" at the front.

Cold rolled steel is accurately finished, and you only need to draw file the edges to remove any nicks or burrs. It may be necessary to do a little hand scraping later, to bring the front and back parallel. The completed carriage will provide the standard for perfecting the ways.

Again, the exact hole centers will have to be taken from your assembly. Space them as shown, and center them in the webb of the bed casting.

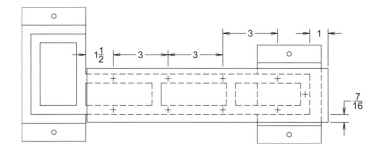

Clamp the ways securely to the bed, and locate the hole centers carefully. Center punch the hole centers, and drill a ⅛" pilot hole through the ways and about 1" into the bed casting. Enlarge the hole to ¹³⁄₆₄", then enlarge the hole in the steel ways to ¼". You can put a ¼" set screw collar on the ¼" bit for a depth gauge, so you won't drill into the bed casting, or you can do it free hand if you are very careful. The drill will stall noticeably when it cuts through the steel, and you can tell when to stop. Tap the hole in the bed for ¼-20 threads, and be very careful, these are blind holes. Countersink the hole in the ways with a high speed countersink, so the head of the screw is a tiny bit below the surface. Do one hole completely, and install the screw before you begin to drill the rest of the holes. When you have two screws installed, the ways won't be able to slip out of alignment. Dump out the drill chips before you begin to tap the holes, and don't oil the tap for these blind holes. It's difficult to clean out the hole if the chips are oily, and you can safely tap aluminum dry if you are careful.

The box ways of the carriage are deeper at the front, so the ways are allowed to hang over the front edge of the bed by ⁷⁄₁₆". The adjustable gib will be in the back ways, so it won't be as deep.

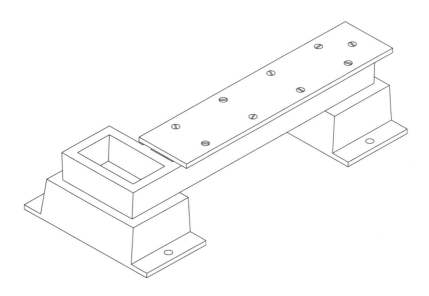

CHAPTER III

THE HEAD STAND

The bed and ways are complete, and you have a firm and accurate foundation on which to build your milling machine. The remaining slides will be either in line with the bed, or at exact right angles to it. The countersunk holes will have a ridge that must be scraped or filed even with the top surface of the ways. Be careful not to distort the edges of the ways when you clean up these holes. Clean them up now, so the top of the ways will be an accurate gauge for the work to follow.

THE HEAD STAND PATTERN

This is the most intricate casting in the project, but splitting the pattern makes it easy to mold. There is still a lot of hand work on this casting, but you can console yourself by remembering that you will soon have a milling machine for this type of work.

Draft is extremely important on this pattern, because it is quite deep at the base. Even so, we can't be as generous as we were with the bed and base because that would greatly increase the finishing work on the casting. Only the screw tunnel has excess draft, and the remainder of the pattern is given draft of 1 degree or less.

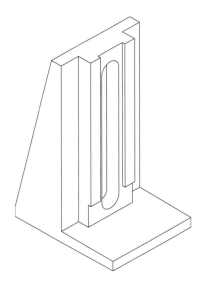

The pattern is split on the vertical plane, and the back portion is the drag half. Two rectangles and two triangles are assembled with glue and brads to make up the drag half, and the cope half is made up of simple rectangular shapes.

Note that the base and triangular parts of the drag half taper ¹⁄₁₆", and the base of the cope half also tapers. The screw tunnel tapers from ⅝" wide to ⅞" wide in both pattern halves. The outside angle at the base of both halves is 90 degrees, and the inside angle is 92 degrees. This is done to save work in filing the base of the casting flat. The patterns are withdrawn from the mold at a slight angle instead of straight up.

THE DRAG HALF PATTERN

The basic section thickness is ½", and white pine is much better to work with than plywood.

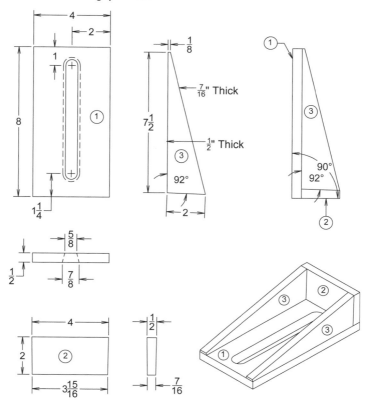

The assembled pattern half is shown as it is layed on the molding board for ramming up the drag. A small fillet is wiped on all inside corners, and the outside corners must be slightly rounded except at the parting plane. Sand a taper of about 3 degrees on the top edge, and round it off well so you can withdraw the pattern at an angle.

The drawing below shows it as it will appear when it is rammed up and the drag is rolled over.

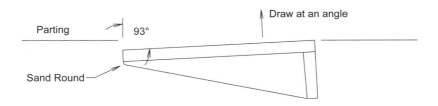

Note also that the screw tunnel is widest at the back, so it will leave a green sand core in the drag.

THE COPE HALF PATTERN

When the drag is rammed up and rolled over, the cope half will be set in place and the cope is rammed up. The halves are aligned by two smooth fitting pins that are made of cut nails. They are cemented into the cope half, and made to fit mating holes in the drag half smoothly, so the halves are well aligned, but will separate easily when the mold is opened up to withdraw the patterns. It is better to have them a bit loose, but not so loose as to spoil the alignment.

When both halves are finished, clamp them together and drill a hole through both halves with a nail that is the same size as the pin. Cut the pins about ½" long, round one end smoothly, and cement them into the cope half. They need extend only about ⅛" from the parting face of the cope half. Then ream the holes in the drag half until the halves will separate easily with no perceptible binding or play.

The same angle treatment is given to the base of the cope half, so that its bottom will be parallel to the bottom of the drag half when the halves are assembled. Its top edge is angled about 3 degrees, and rounded, so it can be drawn in the same manner as the drag half.

Wipe a small fillet on the inside corners, and round the outside corners except at the parting plane. Note the direction of the draft in the screw tunnel. It will leave a green sand core in the cope to mate with the one in the drag.

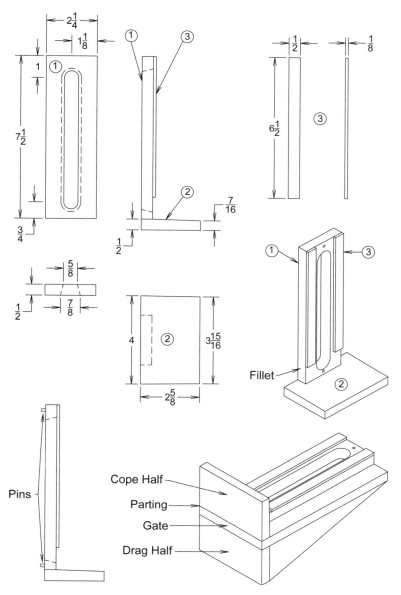

The ½" x ⅛" pads are for mounting the vertical ways. This reduces the amount of surface that must be scraped, and they are left 1" short of the bottom to avoid scraping in a difficult inside corner.

When both halves are assembled, and the pins are installed, lay a piece of waxed paper on the parting face of the drag half, and set the cope half in place. Wipe a small fillet at the junction, to adhere to the cope half. The waxed paper will prevent a bond to the drag half, and you can remove the paper to sand the fillet smooth when the body putty sets up.

Rest the assembled pattern halves on a flat surface to make sure that the bottom is flat. Evaluate both halves for proper draft, sanding a slight amount of draft so each half will be easy to draw from the mold. Fill any flaws with body putty, sand smooth all over, and seal with at least two coats of lacquer or varnish. Make sure the halves are well aligned, and that they will separate easily.

MOLDING THE HEAD STAND

The pins were cemented in the cope half so that the drag half would have a flat surface to lay on the molding board.

Ram up the drag half, following all of the steps, and be especially sure to fill the screw tunnel. Vent generously with the wire, rub in a bottom board, and roll over the drag.

Clean up the face of the drag and set the cope half of the pattern in place. Test it to be sure it will separate easily when the mold is opened.

Dust all over with parting, set a 1¼" sprue pin about 1" away from the center of the base, and ram up the cope. Again, be sure to fill the green sand core area, and vent generously with the wire.

Split pattern molds differ from simple molds in that the cope must be layed down to rap and draw the pattern. If you rap the pattern while the cope stands up, the sand will be weakened, and it will drop out when you close up. Finish the sprue opening to the funnel shape, pull out the pin, rub in a bottom board, and open the mold. Lay the cope down on the bottom board.

The pattern halves should have remained in their respective halves if the pins were properly fit. Swab, rap, and draw the patterns, and clean up the cavities. The gate should be of good size, but smaller than the sprue.

Take special care to clean out the deep cavity, and swab any parts that threaten trouble. Dust the newly swabbed areas with parting, and close up the mold to pour.

Being of heavy section thickness, the metal doesn't have to be quite so hot.

FITTING THE HEAD STAND

The gate is cut off, and the base of the head stand is filed flat so it will rest on the bed casting without wobble.

The vertical pads are scraped true flat to support the vertical ways in the same manner as the bed casting. The vertical ways is a ¼" x 3" x 8½" slab of cold rolled steel, and it is fastened to the head stand with eight, ¼-20 x ¾" flat head screws. A trial assembly must be made before the permanent screws are installed, and that gives you an opportunity to perfect the fit.

File the base of the head stand first. We used extra care in squaring the base angle of the pattern halves so the head stand should rest with the vertical ways exactly vertical. Remove material evenly as you file the base, so the vertical pads won't lean either forward or back.

When the base will rest firmly on the casting, prepare the vertical pads and scrape them true flat. The pads were left 1" short of the base so there would be no inside corner work, and so the base wouldn't interfere with testing on the surface plate.

Drill and tap two ⁵⁄₁₆-18 holes in the center of the ways, and fasten the ways to the head stand with cap screws and flat wash-

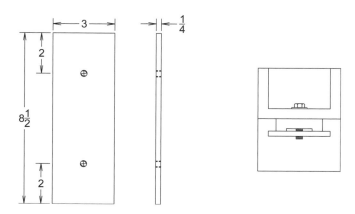

ers through the screw tunnel. This is for the trial assembly, and the holes won't interfere when the bolts are discarded later.

Don't over tighten the cap screws and distort the ways. Just snug them up so the ways won't slip around.

The head stand must be installed so that the ways are at exact right angles to the bed ways, and the front surface is parallel to the bed ways.

The head stand is positioned so that its front edge is even with the front edge of the bed casting. It will be fastened to the bed with

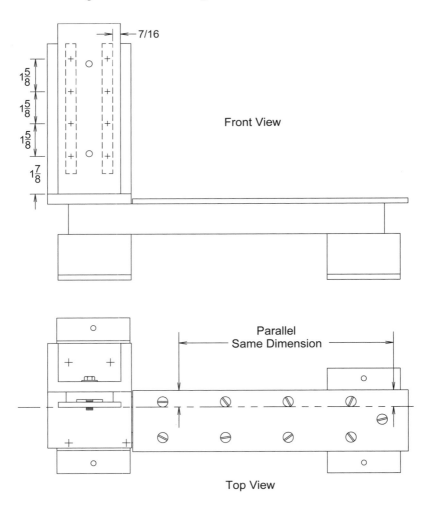

four ¼-20 x 1¼" cap screws with lock washers. The approximate bolt centers are shown page on 56, but you will need to find the exact locations from your trial assembly. The front holes can be drilled from the top, but the rear ones will have to be drilled from bottom of the casting because there is not enough clearance for the drill chuck at the top.

Stain the bottom of the head stand casting so you can scribe the outline of the bed casting when you make the trial assembly. Then it's a simple matter to locate the rear hole centers so that they will fall in the center of the webb of the bed casting. You can stain the top of the bed casting so that the tap holes in the bed can be marked through the holes in the base of the head stand.

Clamp the base securely to the bed, leaving a small gap between it and the bed ways so you can make adjustments. Step drill a $^{13}/_{64}$" hole through the base and about 1" into the bed on the right hand front corner of the base. Locate the hole so it will fall in the center of the webb in the bed.

Enlarge the hole in the base to ¼", and tap the hole in the bed for ¼-20 threads. Install the bolt to help hold the base in alignment as you proceed.

Clamp a straight edge, such as an accurate bench level, to the front of the ways, and adjust the head stand until the front of the vertical ways is parallel to the bed ways. When the distance from the straight edge to the edge of the ways is equal on both ends, it is parallel.

Now you can install the second front screw, and mark the line of the bed on the bottom of the base. Remove the base and locate and drill the two rear holes to ¼". Reassemble, and mark the tap holes on the bed through the ¼" holes in the base. Be sure and check the alignment with the bed ways before you mark the rear tap holes.

Remove the head stand, and step drill and tap the rear holes. Now you can install the head stand with all four cap screws and check the alignment with the bed ways. You may to ream the holes slightly to align perfectly. When all is aligned, install a dowel pin both front and back, so the parts won't be able to shift.

Don't be concerned with the vertical alignment of the ways at this time. When the head stand is permanently fastened to the bed you can make vertical adjustment.

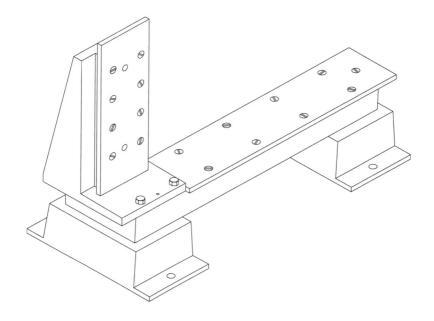

ALIGN THE VERTICAL WAYS

Now you can test the angle between the vertical ways and the bed ways with an accurate square. It's likely that you have nothing better than a carpenters square, but this can do well enough if it is a good one. There is almost certain to be an error in these simple hand operations, but the idea is to hold errors to a minimum by careful work.

You can test a square by drawing a line along its leg, and reversing it to see if the leg falls on the line. If there is no perceptible error, the square is accurate within a small fraction of one degree. Not perfect, but we can live with it for now.

The approximate screw centers are shown on page 56, and note that the ways over hangs by 7/16" on the right hand side. Space them as shown, and center them in the vertical pads. Countersink them slightly below the surface, and scrape off the burrs when complete.

CHAPTER IV

THE SCREW FEEDS

There are a large number of castings left to make, but many of them are identical. It will save time if you make duplicate parts at the same time, even though you are not yet ready for them.

Five hand wheels are used for the screw feeds, and they are all made from the same two patterns. The screw spindles are identical, though the screws will be of different length.

GRADUATED COLLARS

All of the screw feeds are made of ⅜-16 threaded rod, though you can make them of any pitch you like if you happen to have screw cutting gear on your lathe.

It's easy to add graduations to the collars of your hand wheels if you use an existing scale. You can cement the scale directly to the hub of the hand wheel, or you can use a sleeve over the hub so that you can "zero" the collar to any setting.

Since the pitch of the screw is uniform, each full turn of the hand wheel will move the nut by a predictable amount. In this case it will be ¹⁄₁₆", since there are 16 threads per inch of screw. Converted to a decimal, that will be .0625", or sixty two and one half thousandths of an inch. (Divide one by sixteen.) If you divide the hub of the wheel into 62½ graduations, each one will represent .001", or one thousandth of an inch. It will be easier to divide it into 125 equal divisions, to avoid the half graduation, and each graduation will represent .0005", or one half thousandth of an inch.

It would require a very accurate dividing fixture to mark 125 divisions on the circumference of a small hub. The job could hardly be done by hand without serious error, and you will have tried your patience to the limit before you give up in despair. There is an easy way.

By selecting an existing scale of linear divisions, we can machine the hub to a circumference that will accept the required length of linear scale that will give 125 graduations. A metric scale is the most convenient because it is divided in groups of ten. I used a plastic tape measure I found in my wife's sewing box. One side is divided into centimeters, and the centimeters are divided into millimeters.

A 12½ centimeter length will give you 125 equal divisions, and you can cover the existing numbers with liquid paper, and mark more appropriate numbers with a pen.

The hub of the hand wheels are cast at 1⅝" diameter, and it's a simple matter to mount the bored hub on an arbor and carefully reduce its diameter until the length of tape will just exactly reach around it. Then you cement it to the hub, coat it with epoxy or clear lacquer, and you have an accurately divided feed screw collar.

THE HAND WHEELS

While you could use a large ball handle to turn the feed screws, a hand wheel will work much better for a slow even hand feed.

All five hand wheels are identical, and they are easy to make from simple castings.

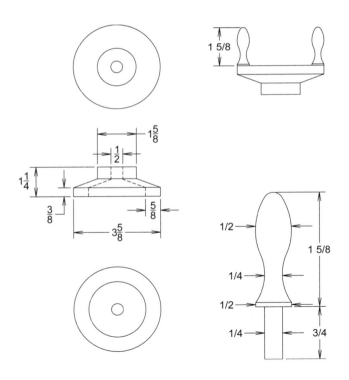

The pattern for the wheel is a simple turning job if you have the threaded taper shank adapter. Simply make the blank from glued up discs of pine, and machine it to size and shape on the lathe. The depression on the top surface can be cut so far as the mandrel nut will permit, and the remainder be removed with a chisel. A length of ½" dowel will close up the hole in the center. The job can be done between centers if you have a spur and cup center for your lathe.

The enlarged view gives you an idea of the anatomy of the finger grips. There are 10 of them, and the easiest way is to make a pattern from a length of ½" dowel rod and cast them in aluminum or pot metal. You can machine them from mild steel stock if you have the patience. A more simple grip can be made from a length of ⅛" pipe and a ¼" x 2" machine screw.

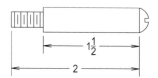

CASTING THE HAND WHEELS

I made my finger grips of cast aluminum, and I used just one pattern. I cast the first one by bedding it into the drag sand with another casting. Just press it into the face of the drag with its ¼" stem against the sprue pin. The stem cavity will serve as the feed gate. You must push the vent wire through the sand in the cavity when the pattern is removed. You could not likely strike the pattern from the surface of the mold, and such a small casting does not have enough pressure from the molten metal to force the gas through the sand. Just remove the pattern and push a very straight and stiff wire into the largest part of the cavity, and right through the sand body. The small wire that is cast on the grip is easy to break off. I used the original pattern along with the first casting to cast two of them in the next mold. Then I used the three castings along with the pattern to cast four of them. Each group was cast along with another part, so there was very little work to casting the finger grips. Each casting is cleaned up to make it suitable as a pattern, until you can cast as many as six in a spray around a single sprue pin. It's a good idea to make several extra in case you spoil some when you fit them to the hand wheels.

The hand wheel is molded in a double roll mold, just as you did for the mounting bases. Use a 1¼" riser in the center of the hub. The pattern will be rammed into the cope, and the core that forms the depression in the face of the wheel will rest on the drag. You can pour through the riser, or you can add a sprue and gate it at the rim.

MACHINING THE HAND WHEELS

The holes for the finger grips can be drilled and tapped, and the casting can be bolted to the face plate for boring the hub, but it will be better to use the bell chuck for the boring operation.

Drill a ⅜" starting hole in the center of the hub, and enlarge it to exactly ½" with the boring tool on the tool post.

Install a ¼" set screw in the hub of the hand wheel, and mount it on a ½" arbor between centers. Face off the top surface and true up the outside diameter. Face off the hub, and reduce its diameter until the 125 mm length of tape measure will reach exactly around it.

INSTALL THE FINGER GRIPS

Step drill and tap two ¼-20 holes in the rim of the wheel, and countersink them on both sides.

Clean up the stems of the finger grips by grinding or filing, and cut ¼-20 threads right up to the shoulder. You can cut threads to the shoulder by turning the die plate over when you have gone as far as you can in the starting position. The countersink in the tapped hole will give you clearance for the very short unthreaded portion. The stem of the grip is not very strong, so you need to do the threading carefully. This is where a couple of extra castings is a good idea.

File the shoulder of the grip so it seats nicely on the rim of the wheel, and screw the grip into its hole. Cut the excess length away, and peen the end of the stem so it will not work loose.

Of course the grips made of ⅛" pipe are stronger, and easier to make and install, but not as pretty.

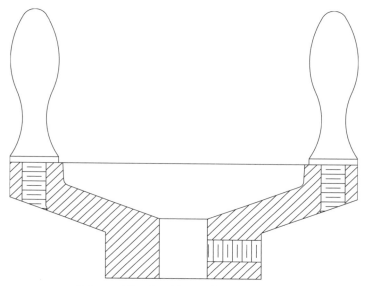

Enlarged Section Through Hand Wheel

THE SCREW SPINDLES

This is a simple between centers lathe job, using ¾" steel stock.

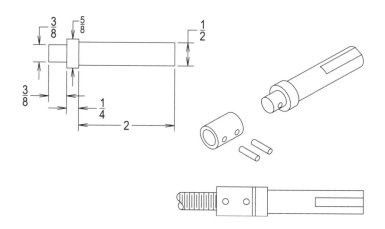

The spindles are coupled to the screws by a sleeve made from a ¾" length of ¼" pipe. Just ream the pipe with a ⅜" drill so it will slip over the end of the spindle and the screw. Then drill a ⅛" hole through each end, and install a ⅛" rivet. The rivet holes are drilled through the screw and the stub on the spindle, and the rivets are peened on both ends. There will be a slight universal joint action in the coupling that will compensate for misalignment.

The screw lengths are: 16" for the cross feed, 11" for the carriage feed, 8" for the head stand, 6" for the tail stand, and 5½" for the compound. These are the actual cutting lengths of the screws, to be cut from standard ⅜" N. C. threaded rod.

The screw supports will be fit with a bronze bushing, and a standard S.A.E. washer is used against the collar of the spindle for a thrust bearing. A thin steel or brass washer should be used between the screw support and the hub of the hand wheel. You can make thin washers of sheet metal, and mount them on a threaded arbor to true up the outside diameter on the lathe.

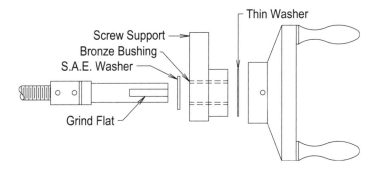

The screws and spindles are assembled as shown above, and the hand wheels are locked to the spindle with the set screw. Grind a flat on the spindle for the set screw to seat against.

If you have ever cut threads on a long slender rod, you know what a job it can be. This simple method works better than anything I've tried to date. It would be the best way to replace the lead screw on your home made lathe if the original screw is not satisfactory.

Acme threaded rod is available, and you can replace the worn out lead screw on a standard lathe by this method.

CHAPTER V

THE SPINDLE HEAD

You'll notice that the photos of my miller show the bearing support screwed to a tongue on the shank of the spindle head slide. That was a poor design, and it proved much easier to cast the shank straight, and screw the support casting to the shank rather than to cast a tongue.

This is another split pattern mold, and the drag half of the pattern also serves to make the casting for the bearing cap.

THE COPE HALF PATTERN

White pine is better than plywood because the plywood is likely to warp.

This type of pattern is easy to make if you cut out the shape of the main body, and fasten the wear pads and clamp pads to it with glue and brads.

The broad flat surface is the parting plane, and only a very slight draft is needed on all vertical surfaces. The outside corners are slightly rounded, except at the parting plane, and wipe a very small fillet on the inside corners.

Note that the clamp pads and wear pads differ in width on each side.

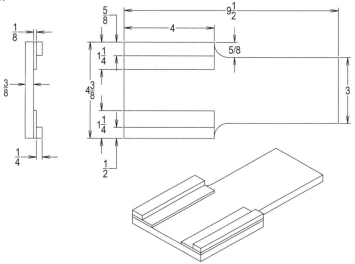

THE DRAG HALF PATTERN

A simple rectangle with a split ¾" dowel rod for the core print. Split the dowel carefully on the exact center, and fasten it to the exact center of the pattern with glue and brads. Sand a minimum of draft all around the pattern.

The split dowel leaves a print in the mold for a 4⅜" length of ¾" steel rod, which is used for the core.

This same pattern serves to mold the bearing cap for the spindle head.

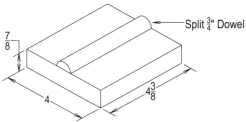

THE ALIGNMENT PINS

The two halves are aligned with small steel pins, just as you did for the head stand. They are cemented into the cope half, so the parting face of the drag half will remain smooth to lay on the molding board.

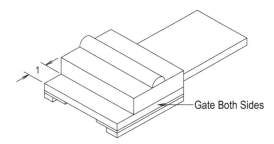

Assemble the two halves with a piece of waxed paper between, and wipe a small fillet at the junction to adhere to the drag half of the pattern. No fillet is needed at the junction of the core print on the drag half.

Make sure the alignment pins fit freely, so the halves will separate easily when the mold is opened.

MOLDING THE SPINDLE HEAD

The steel core is a 4⅜" length, cut from ¾" cold rolled round stock. Bevel the ends slightly, and coat the core with graphite. There is no need to preheat the core.

The steel core must rest in the bottom of the drag, and that is why the smaller half of the pattern is the drag half in this case. Position the drag half pattern so the greater length of the cope half will fall in the flask when you roll over, and ram up the drag in the usual manner. Be sure to ram thoroughly in the corners, and vent generously with the wire. Rub in the bottom board, and roll over the drag.

Set the cope half in place, and set a 1¼" sprue pin about 1" away on both sides of the pattern. One will be the sprue, and the other is the riser.

You will probably need one or more cross ribs in the cope half of the flask. Ram up the cope, finish the sprue openings, vent with the wire, and rub in a bottom board. Open the mold and lay the cope down on the bottom board.

Swab, rap, and remove the patterns, cut the gates in the cope half, and stand the cope on edge to blow out the sprue openings.

Do the usual cleaning and slicking up, and carefully set the steel core in its print in the drag.

Close up and pour rapidly through either sprue. The other sprue will serve as a riser to feed its side.

MOLDING THE BEARING CAP

When the spindle head casting cools, you can knock out the steel core for use in the bearing cap mold.

Just ram up the drag half of the pattern in a smaller flask, vent and roll over, and ram up the cope with a 1¼" sprue pin on each side of the pattern.

The steel core is set in just like the spindle head, and the rest is routine.

FITTING THE BEARING CAP

The mating surfaces of the cap and the spindle head are filed and scraped to a good fit. It is important that the surfaces be flat and true so that accurate adjustments can be made to the bearing fit.

A group of brass shims must be installed in each side of the saddle before it is bored for the bearings. Make up the sets with a mixture of sizes so you can make adjustments of any amount needed. Two each of .002" and .003", and three or four of .001" thickness will make a convenient set for each side. It is much easier to cut the shims to size and clamp them between the members before you drill the holes for the cap bolts.

Four ⅜-16 x 1¾"cap screws fasten the bearing cap to the spindle head. Step drill the holes to ⁵⁄₁₆", right through the cap and about 1" into the spindle head. Then enlarge the hole in the cap to ⅜", and tap the hole in the spindle head for ⅜-16 threads, using the hole in the cap to guide the tap. Don't forget to install one bolt completely before you drill the other holes. Use a flat washer and a lock washer on each bolt.

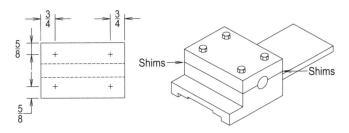

FITTING THE SLIDE WAYS

If you have built the lathe and the shaper, this process is old stuff to you by now. The shaper can be a great help in fitting the slides to the ways because it saves a lot of filing and scraping.

The finished vertical ways provide the test standard for the box slide. If you don't have the shaper, you can lay a piece of abrasive cloth or coarse waterproof sand paper on the ways, and use it to grind the wear pads in the box slide parallel. File the pads first, so they will rest on the ways without wobble, then prepare them for scraping by grinding on the abrasive. A diagonal saw cut in each corner of the box will relieve the corner so it won't interfere with the fitting operation. When the pads have been ground to a near fit, finish by hand scraping. A short length of ¼" x 3" cold rolled will serve as a gauge to file the clamp pads to the correct depth. It can also be the set up gauge for the shaper. The clamps are ¼" x 1" x 4" cold rolled steel, and they are installed with shims so adjustment can be made after wear in use.

The photo shows the shaper making a .050" cut as it planes off the clamp pads for the compound slide. The wear pads have already been planed parallel, and it required only a small amount of hand scraping to finish them. The work is held in the channel vise, and the two nuts are merely furniture to aid in clamping the work. Notice the two set screw collars on the shapers tool post. They added a bit of weight to the clapper to improve its action.

FITTING THE CLAMPS

When the wear pads are scraped to a good fit on the ways, you can cut down the height of the clamp pads until the clamps will hold the slide on the ways without play. Like the saddle for the spindle bearings, the clamps are installed with a set of shims for later adjustment. It is much better to clamp the shims with the clamps, and drill them when you install the bolts, just as you did for the saddle. A set of one .003", one .002", and three or four .001" shims in each side will do the job.

The clamp pads must be parallel to each other and to the wear pads, so the clamps will grip the ways evenly. Just bring them to a near fit with the shaper or by filing, then finish by testing on the surface plate and hand scrape them to true flat. When you have them true, add or remove shims until the ¼" x 3" gauge will fit nicely with the clamps held securely with "C" clamps.

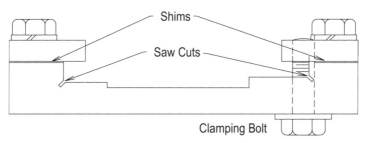

Each clamp is held with four 5⁄16-18 x 1" cap screws. The lowest one on the gib side is installed with its head on the front surface, to serve as a clamping bolt for the vertical slide. It is positioned to draw the clamp against the back surface of the ways to lock the slide. Its threads are tapped in the clamp, while the other clamp bolt holes are tapped in the casting.

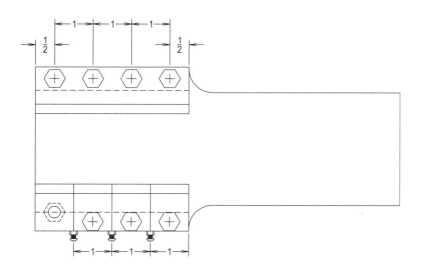

When the slides are brought to a nice fit, position the ¼" x 1" x 4" cold rolled steel clamps on the pads with the shims in place, and proceed to step drill the bolt holes through the clamps and into the casting. Hold the parts securely with "C" clamps, and install one bolt completely before you drill the other holes. The clamping bolt is installed last of all, and it is centered so it just clears the ways. It will be on the lower left as you view the machine from the front.

A ⅛" x ¼" x 3¼" gib is installed in the left side. It's adjusted with three #10-24 gib screws with jamb nuts. The screws are ground to a point, and the point seats in a dimple in the gib. There is little room for error when you drill for the gib screws. The gib is made of ⅛" x ¼" key stock, and a small amount is filed off so it will slide easily in the gib space. Drill through the clamp pads, and allow the drill to cut a shallow dimple in the gib. Install one gib screw completely before you drill the other holes.

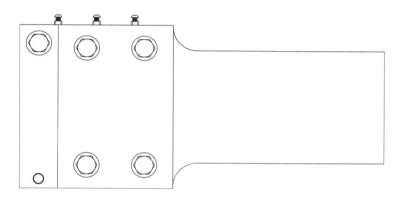

It is likely that you will need to add or remove shims after the clamp bolts are installed. Adjust the clamps so that you have a smooth fit on the vertical ways, without any perceptible play. A slight drag is better than too loose. Then adjust the gib screws to eliminate any side play. The slide should be made to fit well before you attempt to install the feed screw bearing support and tap the threads in the head stand for the feed screw.

All of the box slides will be fit in this same way.

THE FEED SCREW BEARING SUPPORT

A simple pattern, and easy to mold. It requires only minimum draft. Ram it up in the drag, and feed it with a 1¼" sprue, gated at the heaviest part.

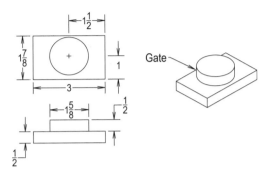

MACHINING THE SCREW BEARING SUPPORT

The face plate angle clamps will serve very well to support the casting for boring.

Very carefully locate the center of the boss, and drill a ⅜" starting hole. Enlarge the hole to ⅝" with the boring bar.

Push a finished bore ⅝" x ½" bronze bushing in the bore, and install a ¼" set screw in the boss.

Mount the casting on a ½" arbor, and face off the end of the boss and the back side.

Reduce the diameter of the boss to match the diameter of the hand wheel hub. (Approximately 1.540").

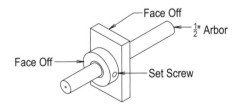

The support is fastened to the shank of the spindle head with two ¼-20 x ¾" flat head screws. The edge must be at right angles so the screw will run parallel to the shank. You can clamp it in the face plate angle clamps and face it off, or you can file it square.

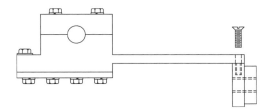

It will be best to install just one screw, then slip a length of ½" shaft through the bushing and align it so the shaft is parallel to the shank of the casting, and also to the box slide. Then you can clamp it securely and install the second screw.

INSTALL THE VERTICAL FEED SCREW

You can make a special center punch by chucking a length of ⅜" steel rod in your electric drill, and grinding the end to a sharp cone. You spin the shaft in the opposite direction of the grinding wheel, so its point will be concentric with the diameter of the rod. There is no need to harden it, since it will only be used to spot holes in aluminum.

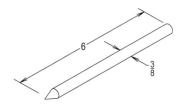

A ½" x ⅜" bushing is slipped into the bushing of the screw support to guide the punch to the center of the tap hole. This simple tool will center all of the feed screw tap holes. It is important that the screw supports be installed so that the screw center runs parallel to the slide, so that the punch will be guided to the proper center. The punch could be made in a lathe if you have a steady rest, and of course it could be ½" diameter to eliminate the need for the ½" x ⅜" bushing, if you have the equipment.

Slide the spindle head assembly onto the vertical slide, and adjust the gib screws for a smooth fit with no play. Be sure that the tap hole is within the limits of the screw tunnel before you punch the center. Slip the bushing in the screw support, slide in the punch, and mark the hole center.

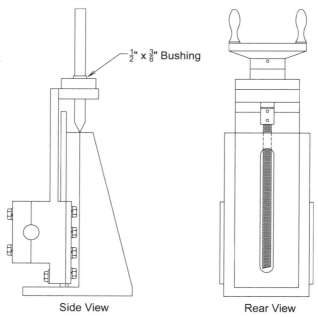

$\frac{1}{2}$" x $\frac{3}{8}$" Bushing

Side View   Rear View

Carefully step drill the tap hole in the top of the head stand to $^5/_{16}$", and tap it for $^3/_8$-16 threads.

Install the 8" screw with appropriate washers, and lock on a hand wheel to complete the vertical slide assembly.

It is important that the slide fit very closely at this point, because you don't want any play in it when you bore the saddle for the spindle bearings. Once the saddle is bored, you can add a shim or two to the clamps to make the slide work a bit more freely.

These methods for fitting the slides and tapping the screw holes will be used for all of the slides, so we won't have to discuss it in detail later.

With the spindle head mounted on the head stand, on ways that are at exact right angles to the bed ways, we have the basic set up for boring the spindle bearing saddle.

CHAPTER VI

THE CARRIAGE AND TEMPORARY WORK TABLE

The miller itself will mill the casting for the permanent work table, but it is necessary to fit the carriage with a temporary table in order to carry out the spindle head boring operation.

The carriage is much like the lathe carriage, and it is the last major job of hand scraping. You will soon have a milling machine to do much of this type of work.

The castings in the foreground of the photo are the universal compound swivel base, the compound slide, and the "Quill" support. These are the basic accessories that give the miller its lathe like characteristics, and they will soon be used to do some of the machining operations that complete the machine.

The quill support is made to fit the compound swivel base as a permanent accessory, but it is bolted directly to the temporary work table for the boring operation.

The compound slide fits the same swivel base, and it is used to convert the miller for such lathe jobs as turning, facing off, and boring.

THE CARRIAGE PATTERNS

This is a split pattern, with the main portion molded in the drag, and the cope half is in two parts. Take extra care registering the cope half at exact right angles to the drag half, to reduce the amount of hand work on the casting.

The basic section thickness is ⅝", and note that the clamp pads and wear pads differ in width. This is to allow for the thickness of the gibs, as in all of the slides.

The screw tunnel is given excess draft, but the rest of the pattern requires only a minimum of draft.

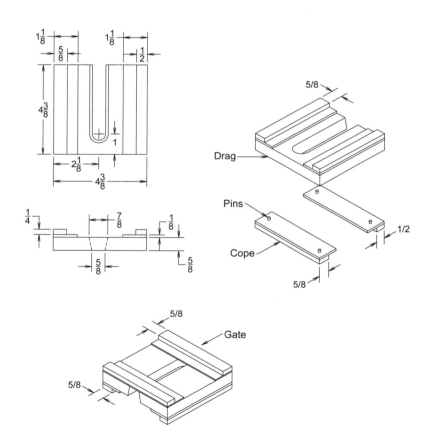

The cope half of the pattern consists of the wear pads and clamp pads, which are identical to those of the drag half of the pattern. Those on the drag are fastened permanently with glue and brads, but the cope half is aligned with pegs, and made to separate easily when the mold is opened.

All of the wear pads are ⅛" x 1⅛" x 4⅜". All of the clamp pads are ¼" thick, but two are ½" wide, and two are ⅝" wide. Note the location of the wider clamp pads on the drawing.

The cope half of the pattern forms the box slide for the bed ways, and the ⅝" clamp pad is on the front. The drag forms the box slide for the work table, and the ⅝" clamp pad is on the left. It's easy to get mixed up because you are molding the casting upside down. Study the drawings so you get it right. The open end of the tunnel will be to the rear when the carriage is installed on the bed. The gib for the bed ways will be on the rear, and the gib for the work table slide will be on the right hand side.

Molding is as for a routine split pattern mold. Set a 1¼" sprue pin about 1" away from the pattern at the point marked on the drawing. Be sure to fill the screw tunnel, and rub in a bottom board to lay down the cope when you open the mold to draw the patterns.

FITTING THE CARRIAGE

The fitting of the slides is identical to fitting the spindle head slide. The finished bed ways are the most reliable test standard for the final scraping.

The clamps are ¼" x 1" x 4¼" cold rolled steel, and each is fastened with four 5⁄16-18 x 1" cap screws with lock washers. They are installed with shims, for later adjustment.

The gibs are ⅛" x ¼" key stock, and each has five #10-24 gib screws with jamb nuts. They are ground to a point that seats in a dimple in the gib.

Make the diagonal saw cuts in the corners of the slides, to eliminate interference as you scrape to fit.

You can use the bed ways as a standard to fit the work table slide, but you will have to do some careful scraping on the left hand side when you bring the work table to exact right angles to the bed ways. Fit the bed ways first, and install its clamps before you begin on the work table slide.

Approximate spacing for the clamp bolts and gib screws is shown in the drawing. Center them so they fall in the center of the clamp pads. Clamp the members together with the shims in place, and step drill to tap size right through both members. As always, install one bolt completely before you begin to drill the other holes in the row. Drill the gib screw holes with the gibs in place, and let the tap drill cut a shallow dimple in the gib. Install one gib screw before you drill the other holes.

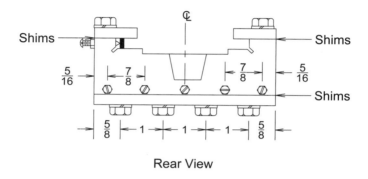

Rear View

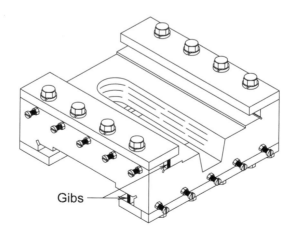

Rear View

ALIGN THE WORK TABLE SLIDE

The work table slide is a 19" length of ¼" x 3" cold rolled steel, and it will serve as the gauge for testing the angle between the bed ways and the work table ways. This must be at exact right angles, and adjustments are made by scraping on the left vertical wear pad of the box slide.

You can clamp a bench level, or other true straight edge, at exact right angles to the bed ways, and bring the assembled carriage and work table ways up close to test the angle. If the straight edge is at exact right angles, and the work table slide is parallel to it, the work table will travel at exact right angles to the bed ways.

This step is very important for accurate face milling. The spindle axis will be exactly parallel to the bed ways, and if the work table does not travel at right angles to it, the cut of the face mill will be concave.

Make sure that the bed way slide is well fit, and that both slides are making full contact on the vertical wear pads on the non-gib sides of the box ways. Adjust the gibs for no perceptible play, and carefully measure the distance at both ends of the test set up. If there is an error, remove the work table slide, remove the left top clamp, and scrape the left vertical wear pad to correct the error. Assemble and adjust the gibs to test again, and repeat until the slide is properly aligned.

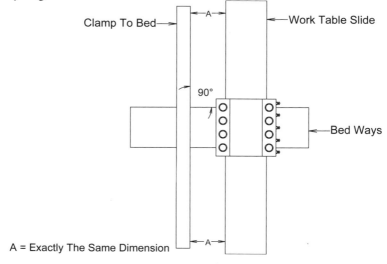

THE CARRIAGE SCREW SUPPORT

The carriage is positioned on the bed by a screw that is very much like the lead screw on the lathe. It is not used as a feed screw though, and its nut isn't split.

The pattern is a simple figure that needs no discussion, except that it should be fed with a 1¼" sprue at the heavy end, which is the circular portion.

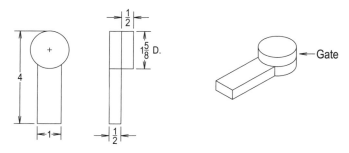

MACHINING THE SCREW SUPPORT

Drill three ¼" holes through the bracket. The two holes that are nearest to the hub are used to bolt it to the face plate. The center hole and the end hole will be used to bolt it to the end of the bed casting.

Use two ⅜" set screw collars as "furniture" to space the casting from the face plate so the boring bar can pass through.

Carefully bore a ⅝" hole in the exact center of the hub, and push in a ½" x ⅝" bronze bushing.

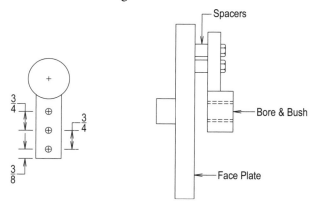

Install a ¼" set screw in the hub, and mount the casting between centers on a ½" arbor to machine the hub.

Face off the hub, and reduce its diameter to match the diameter of the hand wheel hub.

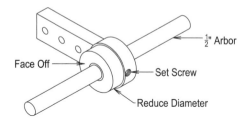

INSTALL THE CARRIAGE SCREW

The screw support casting is bolted to the right hand end of the bed casting with two ⁵⁄₁₆-18 x 1" cap screws with lock washers. The two outside holes in the screw support will guide the tap drill. They are then enlarged to ⁵⁄₁₆", and the holes in the bed are tapped for ⁵⁄₁₆-18 threads.

The screw support is positioned so that it rests on the top of the mounting base, and the center of the screw falls 1⅛" from the edge of the front bed way.

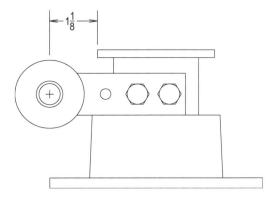

The screw must run parallel to the bed ways, both vertically and horizontally. You can assemble the 11" screw and install it in the support to check its alignment. File the shank of the support casting until the screw is aligned.

THE CARRIAGE NUT

The dimensions here are approximate. You must take exact dimensions from your own assembly.

The nut plate is ¹⁄₁₆" thick steel stock, and it is drilled to match the two left end clamp bolts of the carriage.

The nut is a 1" length of ⅝" key stock, tapped ⅜-16 for the carriage screw, and tapped ¼-20 for the bolt that fastens it to the screw plate.

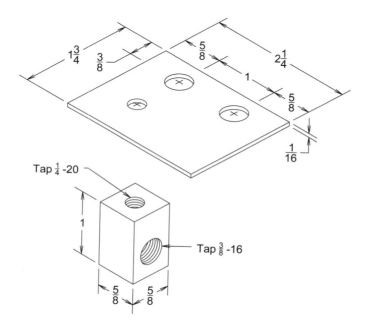

Make sure that the carriage screw is aligned, then bolt the screw plate to the bottom of the carriage with the existing left hand clamp bolts. Locate the ¼" hole for the nut bolt by measuring the center of the carriage screw, and drill the hole. Drill and tap the ¼-20 hole in the top of the nut, and locate the center of the ⅜-16 hole by measuring the center of the carriage screw. Drill and tap the ⅜-16 hole, run the nut on to the screw, and bolt the nut to the plate with a short ¼-20 cap screw and lock washer. Make sure the screw doesn't jamb the carriage screw.

Metal Shop From Scrap Book 4

The 11" screw with its washers and a hand wheel complete the installation of the carriage and screw.

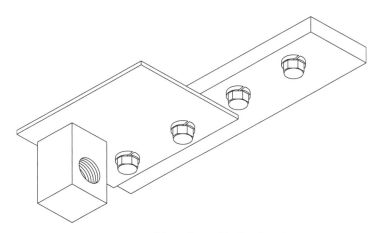

View From Under Carriage

THE TEMPORARY WORK TABLE

A temporary work table is needed to bore the spindle saddle, and for a number of other operations to complete the milling machine and its accessories.

Two 12" lengths of ¼" x 1" cold rolled steel, and two 12" lengths of ½" square key stock are fastened to the top of the ¼" x 3" x 19" cold rolled steel slide to form the work table.

All of the members need to be as near true flat as you can possibly manage. Use the bench level, or other true standard to test them. You can straighten them by laying them on a pair of wooden blocks, and striking another block held on the bowed area. When they appear straight when held to the light with the straight edge, they will be good enough for this phase of construction.

The ¼" x 3" slide can be used later for the permanent table, but you may want to use the temporary table as an auxiliary table for the shaper, or as a bed for a set of bench centers. In either case, the screw support casting can be re-used, and there will be no real waste of material. There is always a need for such material in the home shop.

Use extra care to assemble the parts parallel to the left hand edge of the slide.

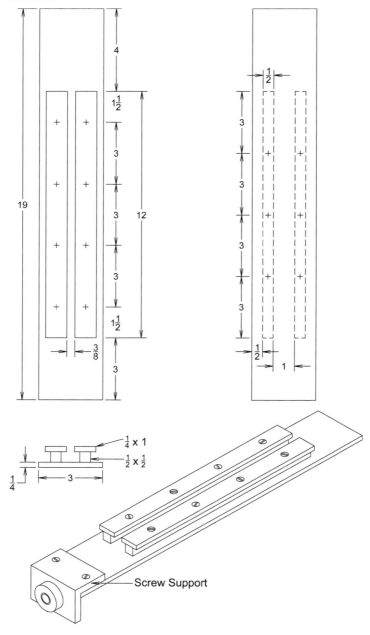

Screw Support

The members are fastened together with ¼-20 x ⅝" flat head screws. It will be best to install the key stock first. Clamp them in position, and step drill a ¹³/₆₄" tap size hole through the key stock and the slide. Enlarge the hole in the slide to ¼", countersink it so the screw will be below the surface, and scrape the burr from the edge of the countersunk holes. As in all stacked assemblies that are joined with a row of screws, install one screw completely before you begin to drill the other holes. Tap the holes in the key stock carefully. Note that the top assembly is located 1" closer to the front end of the slide. You can use ¼" x 1" stock to space the two keys.

The top rails are installed with the screw heads countersunk in the top. They overhang slightly more on the inside, to form a ⅜" wide "T" slot in the center of the table. It will be better to drill the tap holes completely through the slide, to avoid tapping a blind hole, but ⅝" screws are long enough. You can install 1" screws in the four end holes if you feel you need them.

THE WORK TABLE SCREW SUPPORT

The drag half pattern is a simple angle bracket, and the cope half is a 1⅝" diameter cylinder to form the boss for the bearing bore.

The inside of the angle is made true, to reduce labor in finishing the casting. All of the draft is formed on the outside of the angle, and the pattern is drawn at a slight angle. A single pin will align the two halves, and the mold is fed with a 1¼" sprue pin, gated at the edge.

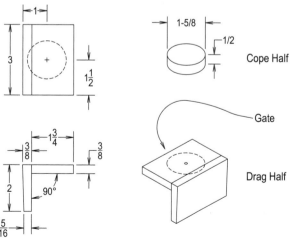

When both halves of the pattern are finished, and the pin is installed in the cope half, assemble them with waxed paper between, and wipe a small fillet to adhere to the cope half at the junction.

Molding is as for a routine split pattern mold, and set the sprue pin about 1" away from the marked location.

MACHINING THE SCREW SUPPORT

Like the other screw supports, it is bored to ⅝" in the exact center of the boss, and a ½" x ⅝" bronze bushing is pushed into the bore. Install a ¼" set screw, and mount it between centers on a ½" arbor to face off the boss and reduce its diameter to match the hand wheel hub.

It can be bolted to a right angle bracket and mounted on the face plate for boring. The object is to bore it so the screw will run parallel to the work table slide.

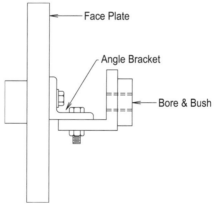

INSTALL THE WORK TABLE SCREW

The screw support is fastened to the work table slide by two ¼-20 flat head screws. (Drawing page 84).

Install the 16" screw with its washers and a hand wheel, and clamp the screw support to the work table slide. Align the screw so that it runs parallel to the slide, and install the screws.

Remove the screw and install the slide in the carriage. Use the special center punch with the ½" x ⅜" bushing to punch the center of the tap hole in the carriage. Make sure the center will fall within the screw tunnel before you punch. Carefully step drill the tap hole to ⁵⁄₁₆", and tap it for ⅜-16 threads. Of course the clamps and gibs must be adjusted so that the slide is in its permanent position before you mark the tap hole.

Install the screw with its washers and the hand wheel to complete the temporary work table installation.

THE QUILL SUPPORT

Early lathes used a quill support on the carriage, and it would be driven by a flat belt that ran on a long drum like pulley that was mounted over head. Others used a round belt that ran over pulleys that were mounted on arms, very much like the sort of thing that dentists use. A rotary cutter or stone could be traveled along work mounted between centers to do many kinds of intricate work.

Its first job on the miller is to support the boring bar to bore the spindle bearing saddle. Later it can be used for radial drilling, dividing, cutting helical gear teeth, or any of dozens of operations that would normally require a universal milling machine.

Ultimately, the quill support will be used with the universal swivel base, but it is bolted directly to the temporary work table for the boring operation.

THE QUILL SUPPORT PATTERNS

Another split pattern, and both halves are multi-use. Like the spindle head, the saddle portion is used to mold the bearing cap. The cope half will be the cope half for the compound slide.

The drag half is a simple rectangle with a split ¾" dowel rod for the core print. Its dimensions differ, but it's made just like the one for the spindle head.

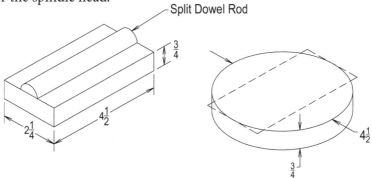

The drag half is centered on the cope half, and two alignment pins are installed. A small fillet is wiped at the junction to adhere to the drag half. Only a minimum of draft is required on both halves.

It will be best to make the disc portion on the lathe, so it will be true round.

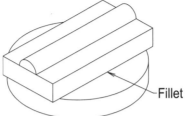

Fillet

MOLDING THE QUILL SUPPORT

We plan to use the half bores as cast, and fit the saddle with ¾" x ⅝" bronze bushings to support the boring bar. A steel core is used in the mold to form the half bores to near size. Shims will be used between the saddle and the cap to bring it to an exact fit.

A 4½" length of ¾" cold rolled steel rod will work, but you will have a better fit if you prepare a special core to .758" diameter on the lathe. The oversize core will compensate for shrinkage, and it will be easier to fit the bar to the bearings.

Molding is as for a routine split pattern mold. Set a 1¼" riser in the center of the disc, and feed the mold at the rim with a 1¼" sprue about 1" away.

Coat the core with graphite, and set it in the mold very carefully.

Use the drag half of the pattern to mold the cap, and feed it with a 1¼" sprue on one side, and a 1¼" riser on the other side. Use the same steel core in the same way.

MACHINING THE QUILL SUPPORT

All of the work on the base of the quill support can be done on the lathe face plate. It will eventually be fit to the compound swivel base, which will have a circular slot centered on 3¼" diameter. The base of the quill support will have two elongated holes to match the circular slot in the swivel base, so we can drill and tap two 5/16-18 holes in the base for mounting it on the lathe face plate.

Saw off the gate and riser, and locate the center of the base as accurately as possible. Scribe a line through the center at right angles to the saddle bore, and locate the two hole centers 1⅝" from the center mark.

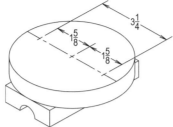

Punch the centers, and step drill them to ¼". Tap the holes for ⁵⁄₁₆-18 threads.

File and scrape the surface of the saddle so it will be true flat. This is necessary for the bearing fit, and also so that it will rest firmly when bolted to the face plate.

Fasten the casting to the face plate with two ⁵⁄₁₆" cap screws through the face plate slots. You can center it by bringing up the tail center to contact the punch mark in the center of the base. The bolts must not come through the casting to interfere with the facing off.

Face off the base of the casting, removing only enough material to clean it up nicely.

Drill a ⅜" starting hole in the center of the base, and enlarge it to exactly ⅝" with the boring bar.

Reduce the outside diameter of the base until a 36 centimeter length of tape measure will reach around it exactly. The tape will have 360 mm divisions, each representing one degree, to provide the protractor divisions when it is used on the swivel base.

All of this work is done without changing the position of the casting on the face plate, so it will be concentric.

When the machine work is done, remove the casting from the face plate, and put a ⅝" plug in the center hole. It should slip in and out easily, without play. Punch it at the center, and use this center to lay out the hole centers for the elongated holes.

Scribe the arcs with the dividers set at 1⅝", punch the centers, and step drill four ⅜" holes on the centers. Scribe arcs to connect the holes, and cut away the waste between the holes with a coping saw. The original ⁵⁄₁₆" holes will be cut away to leave two elongated holes.

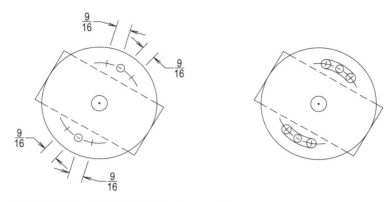

FITTING THE QUILL BEARINGS

It would be better to bore the saddle, but lacking the equipment, we can use the bore that was left by the steel core.

It will be necessary to do a little scraping in the bore to remove any flaws near the ends, and the mating surface of the cap must be filed and scraped true flat.

Make up a set of shims for each side of the saddle, just like for the spindle head, but it is likely that you will need more of them.

Split each of the two ¾" x ⅝" bronze bushings with a hacksaw on one side only, so they can be adjusted.

Slip the bushings onto a ⅝" diameter steel shaft, and set the assembly in the saddle with the bushings even with the ends of the saddle. The splits in the bearings should be on either side, rather than the top or bottom.

Clamp the bearing cap in place with "C" clamps, and add or subtract shims evenly on each side until you feel only a slight drag on the shaft when the clamps are tight.

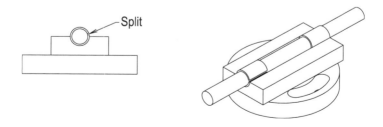

Split

Locate the four bolt centers, punch them, and step drill to ⁵/₁₆"
right through both members. Enlarge the holes in the cap to ⅜",
tap the holes in the base for ⅜-16, and install four ⅜-16 x 1¾" cap
screws with flat washers and lock washers. Be sure to install one bolt
completely, before you drill the other holes, and use the shaft with
its bearings to align the halves as they are clamped together for the
drilling and tapping.

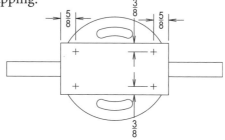

When the bolts are installed you may need to add or remove
shims to bring the bearings to a good fit. This type of bearing installation will wear rapidly in its early life, and a number of adjustments
must be made during a run in period until the shaft is well seated
in the bearings. Once it is broken in, the bearings give good service
for a long time.

Remove the shaft, and drill a ¼" hole to enter near the center of
the bore. Install a spring cap oiler in the hole.

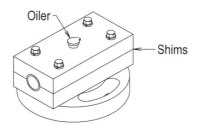

You now have the basic equipment that will be needed to bore
the saddle for the spindle bearings on the head stand, and a permanent accessory that will serve you in many ways.

It will be an easy matter to convert the quill support for use as a
dividing fixture, and you are sure to find many other uses for it as
your shop grows.

CHAPTER VII

FITTING THE SPINDLE

THE BORING PRINCIPLE

It would be impossible to fix the boring bar in a set of bearings that would align it perfectly with the bed unless you had a very costly array of equipment at your disposal. There would certainly be an error in alignment, and if you fed the bar into the spindle head through the bearings, the error would be transferred to the spindle bearing bore.

By fixing the boring bar rigidly on the carriage, and feeding the carriage into the work, the cutting circle will remain on the same center throughout its travel, and it is exactly parallel to the bed ways. Given a rigid support, the only possible error is a slightly elliptical bore. A mis-alignment of as much as one degree would produce an ellipse so slight that it would be difficult to measure with ordinary measuring equipment. It is not difficult to align the bar within one degree of parallel to the bed.

The boring set up is simple, and if you have built the home made lathe you will have all you need to do the job.

THE BORING BAR

The same boring bar that was used to bore the head stock and tail stock for the lathe will do the job. It's a 15" length of ⅝" diameter cold rolled steel with a ¼" square hole ⅜" from one end, and a ¼-20 tapped hole in the end for the set screw.

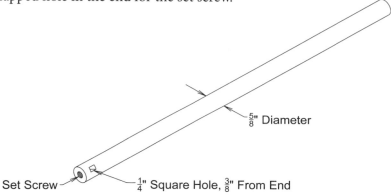

$\frac{5}{8}$" Diameter

Set Screw — $\frac{1}{4}$" Square Hole, $\frac{3}{8}$" From End

Simply step drill a ¼" hole through the diameter ⅜" from one end of the shaft, and using a ¼" square lathe bit for a gauge, file the hole square.

It is easy to get the hole bell shaped, so test with the gauge frequently, and do your best to end up with a smooth sliding fit.

You can improvise a small safe edge file by grinding the sides of a small three cornered file.

When the lathe tool bit will slip freely through the hole, step drill and tap the set screw hole in the end of the bar.

THE BORING CUTTER

You will have to cut a piece of lathe tool off in order to have a cutter bit that is about ¾" long.

Being made of hardened high speed steel, you can only cut it by grinding a groove around it and breaking it off.

Cool the bit frequently as you grind on it. It must not get too hot to hold in your hand, or it will be ruined.

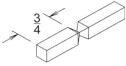

$\frac{3}{4}$

A round nosed cutter that will cut in both directions of travel is the best idea for this job. You will be feeding the carriage by hand, and it will be a help to be able to make a cut on the return pass.

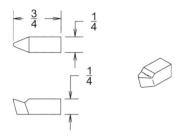

There is no side rake to this cutter, only back rake. The nose is ground to a small radius. You want a razor sharp edge for a smooth cut, so grind on a fine wheel, and finish the edge on a whetstone.

An enlarged view of the cutter in the bore will show you what you are trying to do as you grind it to shape.

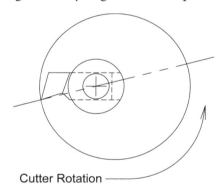

Cutter Rotation

THE BORING SET UP

The photo on page 92 tells most of the story. The boring bar is fixed in the quill support with a set screw collar on each end, and it is driven by the lathe countershaft.

The bar is carefully aligned as near parallel as possible to the bed ways. The countershaft is mounted on the temporary work table with a plywood adapter, and the entire assembly moves with the carriage as it is fed through the bore with the carriage screw. The result is a nearly perfect bore that is exactly parallel to the bed ways.

THE COUNTERSHAFT

The home made lathe countershaft gives a two stage speed reduction, and its lowest speed is ideal for boring the head stand bearing saddle.

If you have not built the lathe, you can use the parts that will be required for the millers transmission to build a temporary countershaft for this job. A pair of pillow blocks, a length of shaft, and the pulleys will give you a two stage reduction to turn the bar at about 150 RPM. Make a simple plywood adapter, and use it in place of the set up that is described here.

If you have the lathe or shaper countershaft, make the adapter of ¾" plywood, and bolt it to the temporary work table with ⅜" carriage bolts in the worktable "T" slot.

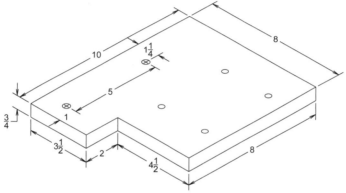

The two holes on the left are on 5" centers, and they are ⅜" diameter. The four holes on the right are layed out to match the base holes of your countershaft. Wait until the quill support is installed and the boring bar is aligned with the bed ways before you install the countershaft.

ALIGNING THE BORING BAR

The object is to set the boring bar as near parallel to the bed ways as possible with simple materials at hand. The procedure is the same as we used for the metal lathe, but the gauge is of different dimensions.

The set up gauge can be made of ¹⁄₁₆" thick steel, and it can be cut to shape and size with a hack saw and a file. The boring bar is ⅝" diameter, so the vertical edge of the gauge will be ⁵⁄₁₆" behind the vertical center of the spindle head bore.

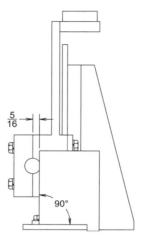

Note that the gauge is made to hook the back edge of the ways, and it is made about 4" tall so it will contact the back surface of the boring bar.

Fit the boring bar to the quill support with a set screw collar on each end for a thrust bearing. The bar should extend about 6" on the left, so it will have ample length to pass through the spindle bore.

Bolt the quill support to the temporary work table with bolts through the "T" slot. The table should be driven within about ½" of its rearward movement so there will be ample area for mounting the countershaft adapter.

Use the gauge to align the boring bar with the bed ways, measuring on both ends of the bar until it is equal. The bar can be checked for run-out by rotating it, and it must be straightened if it runs out more than ¹⁄₆₄".

When the bar is parallel to the bed ways, fore and aft, check its horizontal alignment by measuring the distance between the bed ways and the bar. It is likely that the saddle of the quill support is not parallel to the base, and the top surface of the table may not be parallel. Add shims between the quill support and the table to align horizontally.

This set up procedure may seem crude, but an error of as little as ¹⁄₆₄" would be very apparent to the naked eye. It would result in a mis-alignment of only a fraction of one degree, and that error can be considered negligible for the job at hand. Strive for perfection, and be content with a tiny bit less.

It will be best to install the countershaft and give the bar a generous run in period before you actually begin to do the boring. Oil the quill bearings well, and allow it to run for a few minutes at a fairly high speed. If the bar begins to stall the bearings are too tight, and you must add shims to a proper fit. If it shows perceptible play in the bearings after 10 or 15 minutes of running, remove shims to eliminate the play. When the bar is well seated in the bearings it will run without making a change in the fit. Check the alignment again after the run in period.

It remains only to adjust the height of the spindle head, and you are ready to begin the boring operation. The gib screws of the spindle head should be adjusted so that there is no play in the slide. Raise the head until the saddle center is on the same height as the boring bar, and lock it with the clamping bolt on the left clamp pad.

GAUGING THE BORE

I built my metal lathe without using a micrometer or any precision tools at all. I was not so Spartan in building the milling machine or the metal shaper. I used a vernier calipers to save time. MSC®, U.S. General Supply, Wholesale Tool Co., and many others have inexpensive calipers that are within ordinary means. I got mine from U.S. General for about $13.00, and they are very satisfactory. I've had the plastic ones, but found them a disappointment. It's only a little more for stainless steel, and the small cost is well worth it. A vernier calipers that will read in .001" increments will do the work of an entire set of micrometers.

The spindle head bore will be 1⅛", or 1.125", and all you need to set the cutter on the boring bar is the simple adjustable gauge, a set of feeler gauges, and the calipers.

The body of the gauge is a 2" length of ⅝" key stock, with two ¼-20 holes tapped through. The clamping part is a length of ⅛" x 1" steel strap, bent to a "U" shape on one end, and fastened to the body with two #10-24 screws. The clamp screw and the adjusting screw are ¼-20 threaded rod with thumb nuts on the end. The tapped holes in the body are located ½" from each end. The adjusting screw hole should be deformed by striking the body with a hammer so there will be a slight amount of drag on the screw. The end of the adjusting screw should be slightly convex, and it should be filed very smooth for accurate settings.

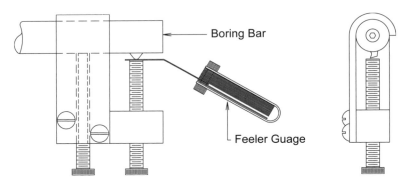

The adjustable gauge is used with a feeler gauge to advance the cutter an exact amount. Simply clamp the gauge on the boring bar with the adjusting screw in line with the point of the cutter bit. Run the adjusting screw lightly against the cutter, and back it off until a feeler gauge of the desired size slips between the screw and cutter without play or drag. Slip out the feeler gauge, and advance the cutter to touch the adjusting screw.

The setting of the cutter depends on an accurate measurement of the bore after the previous cut. Keep in mind that when you measure the bore you are measuring the diameter. When you advance the cutter you are measuring on the radius, and this will effect the diameter by twice as much.

Let's say you have made a series of cuts and the bore is at 1.004". It will require an additional cut of .020" to finish at 1.124". The cutter must be advanced .010" from the setting of the previous cut to increase the bore size to 1.124".

It is best to bore the saddle .001" under size since it is assembled with shims and you can add or subtract them to bring it to an exact fit. A standard finished bore 1" bushing will have an O. D. of 1.125", so bore to 1.124".

It will require a number of passes to enlarge the ¾" bore to final size. Make a light cut to clean up the rough bore, and use the gauges to re-set the cutter after each pass through the bore. Measure carefully, make notes, and compare the results to see if you actually enlarged the bore as much as you intended to. Then you will have perfected your technique before you make the final important cut to finish the bore.

You have ample power to make heavy cuts, but limit them to .020" or .030" on each pass, and make the final cut with very careful study.

The saddle is fit with two 1⅛" x 1" bronze bushings with thrust collars. They are split on one side like the bushings for the quill support.

THE SPINDLE

The outside diameter of the spindle is 1" and it needs a thrust collar on both ends. That's a simple matter, but selecting the type of spindle nose is another matter.

There are a number of spindle nose styles in use, and it can be difficult to choose. Likely, you may find more than one style desirable, and it's no problem to make any type you like. Just look in any good machinery manual or catalog, and take your choice.

The real deciding factor will be the type of cutter and arbor you plan to use. They are available with tapered or straight shanks in several sizes. When the compound slide is finished you can bore any taper within the size limit of the spindle nose, and that includes a #1 or #2 morse taper, or any straight bore within those limits.

The home made cutters that are presented in this manual use a ⅝" straight shank, so a ⅝" straight bored set screw chuck is the most practical beginning. You may elect to make a more elaborate spindle later.

In any case, you should plan to bore all of your spindles clear through, so that you can use a draw bolt when it is needed, and also so you can run a knock out bar through the spindle if a cutter shank gets stuck.

The transmission for the miller has two stages of speed reduction; one fixed and the other adjustable, and the spindle head carries an additional countershaft to provide a second adjustable stage. The change from low to high range is accomplished by interchanging the pulleys on the spindle and the countershaft, so the diameter of the driven end of the spindle is reduced to ¾" to match the diameter of the countershaft.

It's a simple lathe job to make the spindle, and it can be drilled through and bored on the miller.

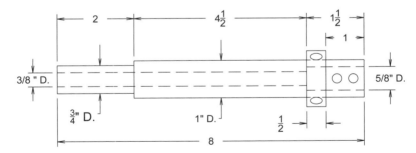

You could begin with 1½" stock, and machine the blank from the solid, but it is much easier to begin with an 8" length of 1" cold rolled steel and fix a set screw collar on the spindle nose end. The standard steel set screw collar will have just one set screw. You should add two more at 120 degree intervals, and they should seat in shallow dimples in the spindle. Both sides of the collar should be faced off after it is locked on the spindle.

The driven end of the spindle uses a ¾" set screw collar with a single set screw. The spindle needs a flat for the set screw to seat against.

If you turn the blank from the 1½" solid it's a simple between centers lathe job, but if you use the 1" shaft you need to drive the work with a perfectly centered chuck, and support the free end with a steady rest. The set screw chuck described in chapter I will work nicely, and if you have built the home made lathe, one of the boring bar supports with a 1" pillow block will serve as a steady rest.

You can also mount the 1" stock in the millers spindle head, and drive it with a 1" bored pulley to reduce the diameter of the driven end to ¾". You can temporarily mount the compound slide from your lathe on the work table, or you can wait until you have made the millers compound before you make the spindle.

DRILLING AND BORING THE SPINDLE

I used the shaft from my "Drill Guide", mounted in the quill support, to drill the ⅜" hole through the spindle. Jobbers length twist drills won't reach through, so you must drill from both ends to complete the hole.

You could remove one of the bushings from the quill support and install the tail stock ram from your home made lathe in its place. Then you can use the hand tight chuck and the taper shank adapter for drilling the spindle hole through. It is not necessary for the chuck to turn, as with the set up in the photo, it only needs firm support in line with the spindle. The improvised countershaft will turn the spindle as you feed the drill with the carriage screw.

Notice the twist drills on the bench in the photo on page 102. A ⅛" bit starts the hole, the ¼" bit enlarges it, the ³⁄₁₆" x 6" extension bit deepens it, the ⁵⁄₁₆" bit enlarges it, and the ⅜" bit finishes it half way through the length of the shaft. The shaft is then turned end for end, and all steps are repeated.

When the through hole is completed you could use the compound from your lathe to bore the ⅝" set screw chuck, but it will be as well to wait until the millers compound is finished for that operation. Two ⁵⁄₁₆" set screw holes are tapped in the nose when the chuck is bored.

Drill a ¼" hole in the spindle head cap to enter the saddle bore at a tangent, and install a spring cap oiler.

CHAPTER VIII

THE TRANSMISSION

I hesitate to admit that it took more than a month to design the transmission, and only a day to build it. It is so simple, and fills the need so well, that it is hard to believe that it was such an elusive problem.

Because the spindle has vertical travel, the countershaft that was used on the lathe won't work. The belt tension would change as the spindle was moved, and it would be a nuisance to adjust the tension for each change of setting.

Furthermore, if the countershaft were mounted rigidly to the bench, the belt tension would strain the spindle head and cause pulsation and alignment problems.

The weight of the motor needed to be removed from the spindle head, and it needed a means for quick speed changes.

All problems were finally solved, and it's a simple type of structure. By mounting the motor on a floating rail, it is free to follow the motion of the spindle head, and its weight becomes negligible because of the leverage. Only a fraction of the motors weight is carried by the spindle head.

One of my main concerns during the development stages of the project was whether a belt drive would work on the final drive. I really wanted to avoid gears because they are so expensive, and our shop has not developed to the point where we can make them. The logical alternate to gears would be a chain drive, but still a bit costly. I'm happy to report that the belt drive works very well, even at the lowest speed of 43 RPM. I've made some abusively heavy cuts, and see no sign of trouble with the belt drive so long as the feed rate is held within reason. Of course the belt drive can stall if the cut is too deep and the feed rate is excessive, but you can make a .050" cut with the face mill set at 3" diameter, and that exceeds the needs of most home operations.

The motor is a ⅓H.P. 1725 RPM split phase, or ¼ H.P. would probably work as well. I got mine from an old wash machine.

The motor pulley is 1½", and the first stage counter-shaft pulley is 8" for a reduction ratio of 5.33 to 1. This gives the first stage countershaft a speed of 324 RPM.

The second stage of reduction is through a pair of step pulleys of 5"-4"-3"-2" diameter. The ratios are 1 to 2½, 3 to 4, 4 to 3, and 2½ to 1. The second stage counter-shaft speed can be 130 RPM, 243 RPM, 432 RPM, or 810 RPM.

The final stage pulleys can be interchanged for a ratio of 3 to 1 or 1 to 3. You can also use a pair of sprockets and a chain for the final stage if you plan on doing heavy work on a regular basis.

Eight speeds are available in two ranges. Low speeds are 43 RPM, 81 RPM, 144 RPM, and 270 RPM. High speeds are 390 RPM, 729 RPM, 1296 RPM, and 2430 RPM.

Plans for guards have not been included, but it would be wise for you to add them to your machine for your safety. Open belts and chain drives are extremely dangerous, and the possibility of serious injury demands extreme caution. Your fingers or clothing can be caught up before you know what is happening, and there is ample power to do serious damage. A switch should be located so you can shut down in an instant.

The second and third stage reductions have a quick change movement that uses the same toggle principle as the lathe countershaft. The pivots pass an over center point where motion is stopped, and the tension of the belt locks up the mechanism. There are no springs or catches, and standard hardware items together with four castings are all you need.

THE SPINDLE HEAD COUNTERSHAFT

Specially made pillow blocks are mounted on angle iron brackets to support the countershaft. The brackets pivot on parallel arms that are pivoted on brackets bolted to the spindle head. A diagonal toggle link lowers the pillow blocks to release belt tension, and raises them to tighten the belt. A stop is riveted to the mounting bracket to limit the travel of the release lever and lock it in the over center position.

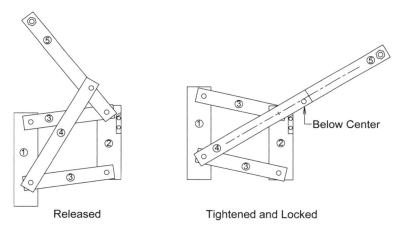

Released   Tightened and Locked

The pillow block brackets and the mounting brackets are 1¼" x ⅛" angle iron, and the arms, links, and levers are ¾" x ⅛" strap iron. The pivots are ³⁄₁₆" iron rivets.

Note that all of the pivots are centered in the members, except the upper pivot of the toggle link, which is drilled below the center.

There are four parallel arms, all identical, and the remaining members are made in matched pairs.

The release lever stops are made of ¼" x ⅛" stock, and they can be cut from any scrap on hand. Fasten them to the mounting brackets with ⅛" rivets.

The upper and lower pivots of the diagonal links require washers so that they clear the pivots of the release levers and upper parallel arms. Study the top view drawing for the arrangement and positioning of the members, and note that the lower parallel arm and the diagonal link share the same pivot, and so do the upper parallel arm and the release lever.

The pillow block brackets both angle to the right, but the mounting brackets are opposed.

The release lever handle is a 4½" length of pipe with a length of ¼" threaded rod to fasten it between the levers. A wooden bushing in each end will center the rod.

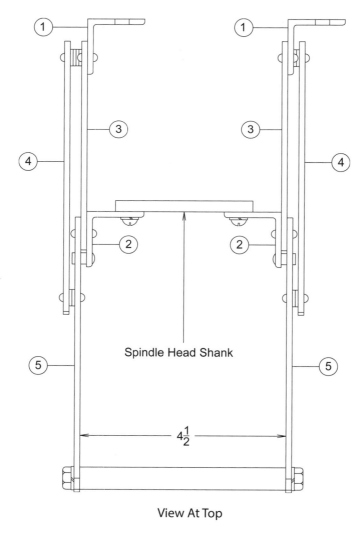

Spindle Head Shank

$4\frac{1}{2}$

View At Top

Lay out all of the parts carefully, and step drill the pivot holes to
³/₁₆". The mounting holes are ¼", but it will be better to drill ⅛" pilot
holes to guide the drill for drilling the tap holes in the spindle head
shank during final installation.

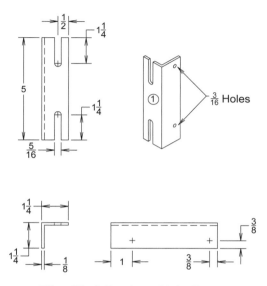

Pillow Block Brackets, Make Two

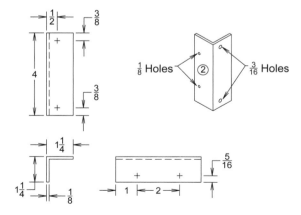

Mounting Brackets, Make Two

Make the parallel arms as near identical as possible. It is best to lay them out and drill them separately unless you have a drill press and can clamp them securely together.

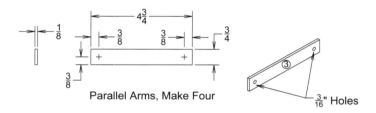

Parallel Arms, Make Four

$\frac{3}{16}$" Holes

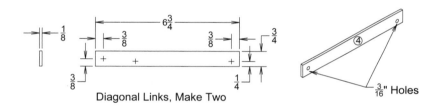

Diagonal Links, Make Two

$\frac{3}{16}$" Holes

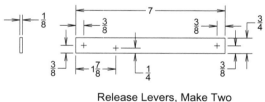

Release Levers, Make Two

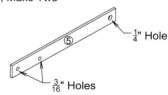

$\frac{1}{4}$" Hole

$\frac{3}{16}$" Holes

Metal Shop From Scrap Book 4

Notice that the upper pivot hole in the pillow block brackets are ⅜" from the top. The lower pivot holes are 1" from the bottom. Rivet a parallel arm to the top pivot hole of each pillow block bracket.

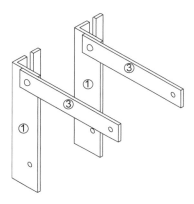

Notice that the mounting brackets oppose, while the pillow block brackets both face to the right. Rivet a parallel arm to the lower pivot hole of each mounting bracket.

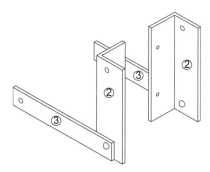

Peen the rivets well so that the peened end is no larger than the head, and make the joints tight. It will take only a drop of oil and some movement to free up the pivots.

Notice that the upper pivot hole in the diagonal link, and the link pivot hole in the release lever are ⅛" off center. Rivet the upper link pivot and the release lever link pivots together to make an opposing pair, with enough close fitting washers to space the members ⅛" apart.

Join the mounting bracket upper pivot, the upper parallel arm, and the lower pivot of the release lever to make an opposing pair of assemblies.

Finally, join the lower pillow block bracket pivot, the lower parallel arm, and the lower pivot of the diagonal link. Use enough close fitting washers to make sure the diagonal link will clear the rivet at the lower release lever pivot.

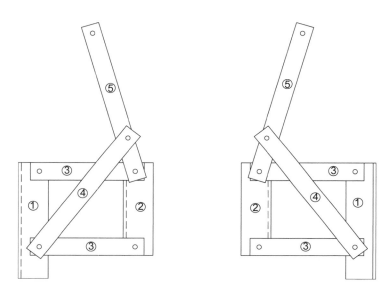

Make the release handle of a 4½" length of ¾" O. D. pipe, and fit each end with a wooden bushing to center the 5½" length of ¼" threaded rod. Join the two halves of assembly with the handle and a nut and lock washer on each end. See top view on page 106.

Clamp or bolt a scrap of metal or wood to the pillow block brackets to properly space the members, and clamp the assembly in position on the spindle head shank to drill the tap holes through the ⅛" pilot holes in the mounting brackets. The bottom of the mounting brackets should clear the spindle head saddle by about ⅛". See the photo on page 102. Make sure all is well aligned, then step drill to tap size for ¼-20 threads, enlarge the holes in the brackets to ¼", and tap the holes in the spindle head shank.

Bolt the assembly to the shank with ¼" x ½" bolts.

THE SPINDLE HEAD PILLOW BLOCKS

The second stage release crank must pivot concentrically with the spindle head countershaft, so the pillow blocks are made with a journal.

Both pillow blocks are identical, and one is inverted to make an opposing pair.

The pattern is very simple, and requires only minimum draft. Fit a short pin in the end of a 1¼" sprue pin, and drill a locating hole in the pattern so the pin will register the riser in the center. This serves as a riser, or "sinking head", and it is also the pouring gate.

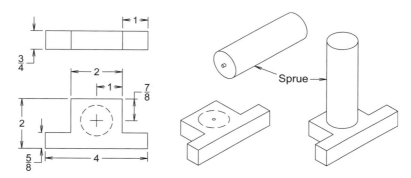

MACHINING THE PILLOW BLOCKS

The riser provides the stock for the journal, so allow about ¾" of it to remain on the casting when you saw off the sprue.

The face plate angle clamps will hold the casting as it is bored for its bushing. Locate the boring center 1⅛" above the base, and in the center of the boss. Bore it to ¾", push in a ¾" x ⅝" bushing, and install a ¼" set screw. These set screw holes will later be used for the oil caps, so put them on opposite sides to make an opposing pair.

Mount the casting between centers on an arbor, face off the journal side, and reduce the diameter of the journal to exactly 1". A standard steel 1" set screw collar is ½" thick. Use it for a gauge to cut a groove in the journal for the retaining ring. A hack saw will cut the groove, and it should be about ¹⁄₁₆" deep. Try the ring in it until it is the right depth.

Step drill a ⁵⁄₁₆" hole in each mounting ear on 3" centers. Remove the set screws, enlarge the holes to ¼", and install spring cap oilers in place of the set screws.

Slip both pillow blocks onto a ⅝" shaft and file the bases of the pillow blocks parallel.

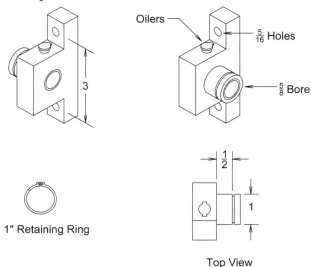

Oilers

$\frac{5}{16}$ Holes

$\frac{5}{8}$ Bore

3

1" Retaining Ring

$\frac{1}{2}$

1

Top View

THE SECOND STAGE RELEASE CRANKS

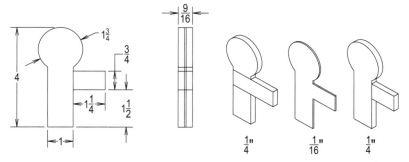

$1\frac{3}{4}$

$\frac{3}{4}$

4

$1\frac{1}{4}$

$1\frac{1}{2}$

1

$\frac{9}{16}$

$\frac{1}{4}$" $\frac{1}{16}$" $\frac{1}{4}$"

Both sides of the casting will be faced off, and the finished crank must be ½" thick, so the pattern is made ⁹⁄₁₆" thick. You can make it of solid stock, but a laminated pattern can be made with ¼" stock and ¹⁄₁₆" cardboard between. Note the staggered joints for the laminated plan.

Assemble the laminated pattern with glue. Only a slight amount of draft is needed, and feed the mold with a 1¼" sprue at the 1" leg.

MACHINING THE RELEASE CRANK

Drill and tap two 5⁄16-18 holes, mark the center of the circular part, and mount it on the face plate with two 5⁄16" cap screws through the face plate slots. Use 3⁄8" set screw collars for spacers, so the boring bar can pass through.

Bore the circular part to 1" to fit the journal, face off the first side just enough to clean it up, and invert it on the face plate to face off the second side. Reduce its thickness to ½".

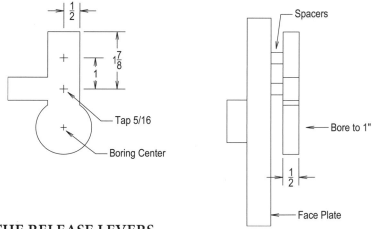

THE RELEASE LEVERS

The release cranks are identical, but the levers are on opposite sides to make an opposing pair.

The lever is bolted to the crank through one of the tapped holes, and a second bolt is installed in the tail.

A 3⁄8-16 hole is tapped for the pivot, and the corner of the crank is filed or ground to a ½" radius so it will clear the motor rail.

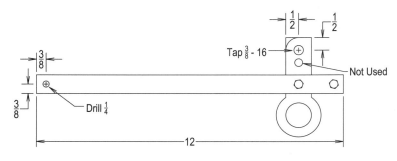

THE SPINDLE HEAD COUNTERSHAFT

You can use an 8" length of ⅝" cold rolled shaft and a ¾" x ⅝" split steel pulley bushing, or you can prepare the shaft with a ¾" diameter stub to adapt it for the ¾" bore of the pulleys.

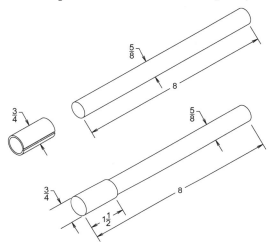

INSTALL THE COUNTERSHAFT

The spindle head countershaft carries a 5", 4", 3", 2" step cone pulley between the pillow blocks, and a 2" x ¾" bored pulley on the left outboard end, to line up with the 6" x ¾" bored pulley on the driven end of the spindle.

The outboard pulleys are interchanged to change from low to high speed range. That is why the outboard ends of the spindle and the countershaft are made the same diameter.

The pillow blocks are mounted to the brackets with ⁵⁄₁₆" cap screws through the slotted holes in the brackets. The cap screws thread into a sliding nut plate made of a length of ⅛" x ¾" strap iron.

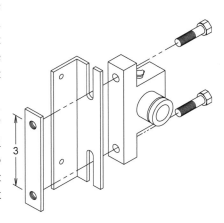

The sliding nut plate is tapped ⁵⁄₁₆-18 to match the hole center spacing of the pillow blocks.

INSTALL THE RELEASE LEVER STOPS

The upper pivot hole of the diagonal link is ⅛" off center, and so is its anchor hole in the release lever. As the lever is drawn forward, the pivot will pass over the center of the release lever pivot, and the pillow blocks will be at the highest point just as it passes center. The lever is stopped at a point slightly over center, and the tension of the belt locks it in the over center position.

Install the pulleys on the outboard end, and fit them with a belt. Mine used a 28" belt, but your assembly may be a little different. The slotted holes in the brackets allow for adjustment, and the pillow blocks should be adjusted to bring the belt snug when the release lever is parallel to the diagonal link.

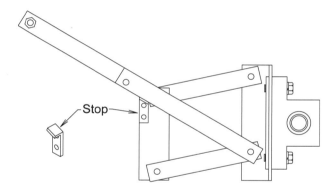

Clamp the stops in place to test for the proper over center position, then install them permanently with rivets.

Flats should be filed or ground on the countershaft for the pulley set screws to seat against before you lock them in place permanently.

THE MOTOR RAILS

These are 14" lengths of 1¼" x ⅛" angle iron, and they are supported on the end by uprights made of the same size angle. A pair of pillow blocks are bolted to the top of the rails, and the motor mounting bracket is hung under the rails to make up the first stage speed reduction. The release crank is pivoted at the end of the rails so that it will draw the shaft centers together to release belt tension.

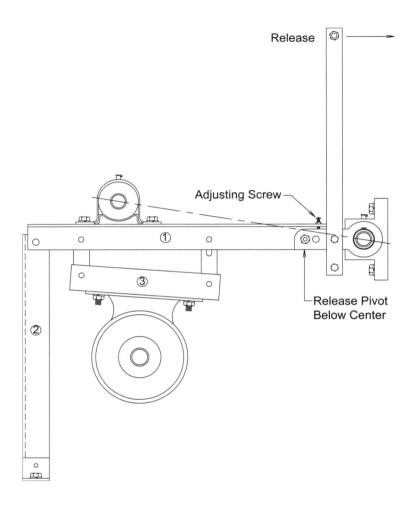

A pair of ⅝" pillow blocks carry a 9" shaft fitted with a 5", 4", 3", 2" step cone pulley between the bearings, and an 8" outboard pulley. The motor is fit with a 1½" pulley, and the first stage belt tension is adjusted by the slotted links. My first stage belt is 32", the second is 35".

The drawing shows the release pivot farther below center than it will be when finally adjusted. The adjusting screw will limit the return motion so that the release mechanism is locked at a point just over center.

I used Dayton #2X529 pillow blocks, and I discarded the rubber pads that are furnished with them. Any pillow block that has a center height near 1" will work just fine.

THE RELEASE CRANK PIVOTS

A cutaway view from the front shows the release cranks as they pivot on ⅜" x 1½"cap screws. Flat washers are used for spacing and to take up the excess thread length. A jamb nut locks the pivot bolt after adjustment.

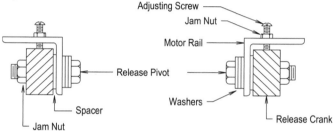

ASSEMBLE THE RAILS AND LEGS

The legs and feet are identical, and one of each is inverted to make an opposing pair. The rails must be layed out, drilled, and tapped as an opposing pair.

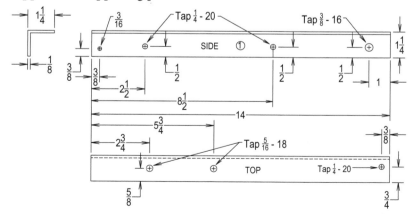

The legs are simply 12" lengths of 1¼" angle, and the feet are of the same size angle iron.

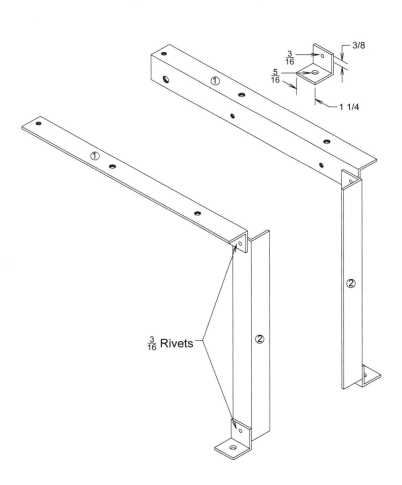

THE MOTOR MOUNTING BRACKET

Electric motor bases have different spacings of the slotted holes, but the most common layout is 2¾" x 4¼" as found on old wash machines etc. Check your motor base before you drill the spreaders for the bracket.

Two solid links and two slotted links suspend the bracket from the motor rails. Make them of ⅛" x ¾" strap.

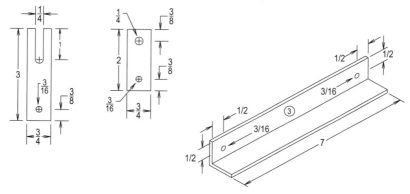

Rivet the links to the brackets to make an opposing pair.

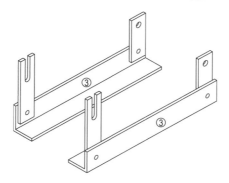

Install both release levers on the journals with the retaining rings, and clamp the motor rails parallel. Measure the distance between the rails, and make two spreaders of ⅛" x ¾" strap ⅛" shorter than the distance.

Measure the center distance between the motor base slots, and drill a pair of ⅛" holes in the spreaders to match the slot spacing.

Clamp the spreaders to the brackets so that the pilot holes form a rectangle to match the slot spacing on the motor base, and drill the pilot holes through both of the brackets.

Enlarge the holes to $^{13}/_{64}$" through both members, and separate the members to enlarge the holes in the spreaders to ¼".

Tap the holes in the brackets for ¼-20 threads, and assemble the members with ¼" x 1¼" cap screws with lock washers.

The ends of the screws will form studs on the correct spacing for the motor base slots.

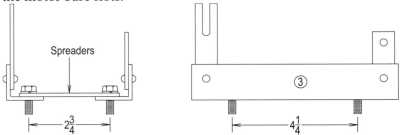

Install the assembled motor bracket on the motor rail as seen on page 116, and install the motor. Short ¼" cap screws with lock washers will fasten the solid links. Use a flat washer to cover the slot on the slotted links.

Now you have all you need to complete the transmission and install the pulleys and belts.

Align everything carefully, lubricate all of the bearings, and install a switch at a convenient place so you can operate the miller safely.

Give some thought to guards for the belts and pulleys, and mount the machine in its permanent location now.

THE END IS IN SIGHT

At this point you have nearly as much as you would have if you had purchased a milling machine. It remains only to bore the spindle nose chuck, install a couple of set screws, and you can begin to do some milling operations.

This is only the beginning though, for you will soon be needing an array of fittings and accessories, and a selection of cutting tools.

You have all you need to make them though, so don't run to the store yet. There's more fun in the offing.

CHAPTER IX

THE UNIVERSAL COMPOUND

The universal compound, which is not normally a part of a milling machine, is what gives you the ability to bore the chuck, make your own cutter blanks and holders, and machine many of the parts that will go to complete the miller and its accessories. You can also fit the spindle with a large diameter face plate to do some jobs that are too large for your lathe, and you have a range of spindle speeds that is slow enough for such work.

THE UNIVERSAL BASE

The universal base adapts to the compound slide base, the quill support base, a swivel base vise, or any special fixture you might need for an unusual job. It expands the range of capability to jobs that would normally be done on a universal milling machine.

The pattern for the base may seem complex at first, but it is a simple job to make the main body on the lathe face plate.

It requires only a minimum of draft on the outside, but the inside surfaces are sloped ⅛" for easier molding.

I found it easier to form the circular portion on the lathe, and add the rectangular parts, than to form the entire pattern from the solid.

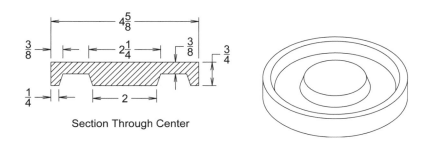

Section Through Center

When the circular portion is formed, cut a pair of rabbets in the rim to install the ears with glue and brads.

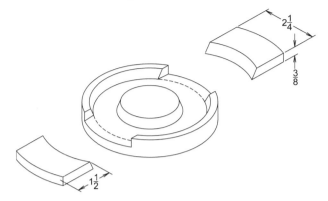

When the glue is well set, trim the outside diameter of the ears to 6½".

A pair of tie bars are added to the pattern, because a ⅜" wide slot will be cut through the casting, and the tie bars will join the rim to the center section.

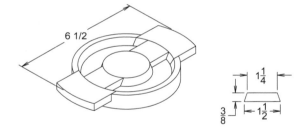

The tie bars are cut to approximate size, and the gaps that are left by the poor fit are filled with plastic body putty. Form a fillet with a ⅛" radius on all of the inside corners of the cavity. This portion of the pattern leaves a green sand core, and it must be very smooth and well drafted. Any humps or undercuts will cause the core to break up when you draw the pattern. Sand only a slight amount of draft on the outside of the pattern. Sand very smooth all over, inside and out, and seal with at least two coats. A light sanding with fine sand paper after the sealer dries is a help on all patterns.

MOLDING THE UNIVERSAL BASE

If your sand has good bond this pattern can be molded in the drag, but that will leave the green sand core suspended from the face of the cope when you open the mold.

A 1¼" feed riser must be used in the center of the mold because of the heavy center section, and it would better to make a false cope so that the core will rest on the face of the drag.

Lay the base of the pattern on the molding board and ram up the cope first. Rub in a bottom board and roll over the cope. Ram up the drag, vent generously with the wire, rub in a bottom board, and roll over the entire mold.

Now you dump out the false cope, set the riser in the center of the pattern, set a 1¼" sprue pin about 1" away from either of the ears, and ram up the new cope.

Be careful not to strike the riser as you ram up the new cope, so that the pattern will remain in the cope when you open the mold.

Remove the sprue pin and riser, and rub in a bottom board so you can lay the cope down to draw the pattern.

You want the green sand core to be firm, but well vented. This casting gets a lot of machine work, and you don't want any sand inclusions in it, so clean up carefully before you close up to pour.

MACHINING THE UNIVERSAL BASE

All of the work can be done on the face plate, and you saw some examples in the photographs in chapter I.

A circular slot centered on 3¼" diameter will be cut in the face of the casting. If it were not for the tie bars, the center of the casting would fall out when the tool cut through the ⅜" thick webb. A pair of ⁵⁄₁₆" holes are tapped on the 3¼" diameter, and centered in the tie bars, to be used for mounting the casting on the face plate. They will be partly cut away when the slot is cut later.

Cut off the riser with a hack saw, as close to the surface as you can. Locate the center of the circular part of the casting, and scribe a line through the center of the area in line with the ears and the tie bars.

Step drill and tap two ⁵⁄₁₆-18 holes on 3¼" centers and step drill a ⅜" hole in each ear on the same center line. Be extra careful with this very important layout.

The first operation will be to face off the base, and the casting is mounted on the face plate with 5/16" cap screws through the face plate slots, using a pair of set screw collars for spacers so the stub of the riser won't interfere.

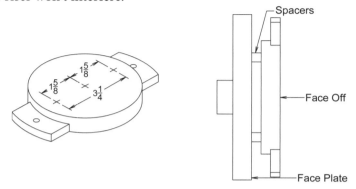

Use extra care in mounting the casting for facing off the bottom surface, and remove only enough metal to clean it up.

When the bottom surface is faced off clean, remount it with the bottom snug against the face plate, and bring up the tail center to position the center of the casting.

All of the remaining work must be concentric, so the casting must remain in its second position until all work is completed.

Drill a ⅜" starting hole about ½" deep in the exact center, and bore it to ⅝" for a close fit on the pivot pin.

Reduce the outside diameter until a 360 mm length of tape measure will reach exactly around it. Face off the top surface of the ears at the same time.

The most difficult operation is cutting the ⅜" wide slot through the webb. The cutting tool resembles a parting or cut off tool, and its edge can only be about ⅛" wide. It has no back rake, and only a very tiny relief on the end and the sides. An enlarged view will give you an idea of how to grind the tool bit.

Notice that the end is slightly wid-

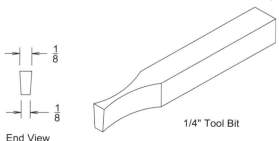

er at the top, and the tool is narrowed behind the point for clearance. The end relief should be about 1 degree so that the edge won't take a deep cut.

The outside diameter of the slot will measure $3\frac{7}{16}$", and the inside diameter will measure $3\frac{1}{16}$". A series of narrow cuts are made to the full width of the slot, then a second series, a third, etc., until the cutter breaks through to the cavity. A small amount will be cut from the top surface of the tie bars, but don't cut so deep as to weaken them.

If you set the lathe compound slide parallel to the bed ways, you can feed the depth of cut with the compound, and the width of the cut with the cross feed.

Only very shallow cuts can be made, so be prepared to spend considerable time on this operation.

Face off the top surface, and relieve the center portion slightly so the accessories will bear on the outside diameter of the base. The bases of the accessories should also be relieved in the center.

It may be necessary to scrape the cavity on the under side so that a "T" bolt will slide smoothly. You can make the "T" bolts from carriage bolts or cap screws.

THE COMPOUND SWIVEL

The circular cope pattern for the quill support will be the cope half of this pattern. The drag half of the pattern is a simple rectangle with a screw tunnel.

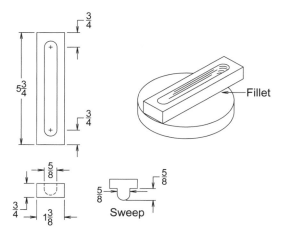

The tunnel is ⅝" wide at the top, and ⅝" deep. It must be well drafted so the green sand core will release.

I drilled a ⅝" hole right through on each end, and cut an elongated hole through the entire pattern. Then I clamped a block to the bottom with waxed paper between, and formed the tunnel bottom with body putty and a simple sheet metal sweep.

After the first application of putty sets up, the sweep serves as a formed scraper. One or two more applications of putty will fill the flaws, and the inside of the tunnel is sanded very smooth.

Like the quill support, the pins in the cope half register in holes in the drag half. Press the new drag half against the existing pins to align it on the center line of the disc, and drill and ream the holes for a smooth fit. One end of the drag will be just even with the diameter of the disc.

Assemble the two halves with waxed paper between, and wipe a small fillet to adhere to the new drag half.

Molding is exactly the same as for the quill support, including the 1¼" sprue and riser. Take extra care to press the screw tunnel full of sand, and vent generously.

MACHINING THE COMPOUND SWIVEL

Drill and tap two ⁵⁄₁₆-18 holes in the disc on 3¼" centers just like you did for the quill support.

Center the casting on the face plate to bore the ⅝" center hole, and reduce the outside diameter until the 360 mm tape measure fits exactly around it. Face off the base and relieve the center portion to match the universal base.

Finally, mount the finished base on the face plate and true up the top surface of the pad.

Form the circular elongated holes in the base just as you did for the quill support.

THE COMPOUND SLIDE WAYS

The ways is made of a 7" length of ¼" x 2" cold rolled steel, fastened to the pad of the swivel with six ¼-20 x ¾" flat head screws. There is scant room for the tapped holes on either side of the tunnel, so the hole centers must be layed out with extreme care.

The top surface of the pad must be tested and scraped true flat before the ways are installed.

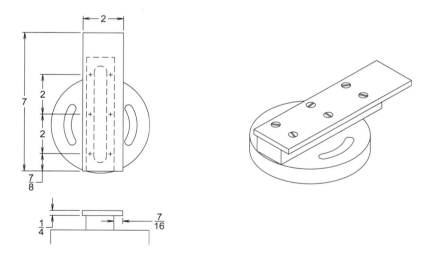

Align the ways carefully, and clamp securely as you step drill and tap the holes. Same procedure as for all slides.

THE COMPOUND SLIDE

Another split pattern, and the cope half has two parts. The drag half will also be for the tail stand slide, but it will use a different cope half, and the screw support will be different.

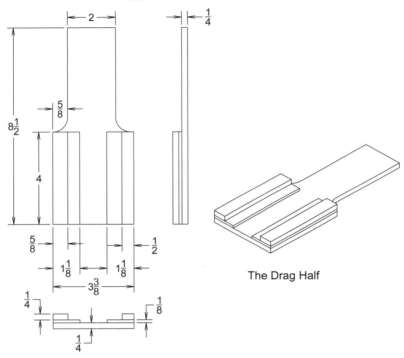

The Drag Half

Two simple rectangles form the cope half, and they are each aligned with two small pins made of brads. A small fillet is wiped at the junction to adhere to the cope halves.

It's a routine split pattern mold, with the main portion rammed in the drag. The two cope parts are

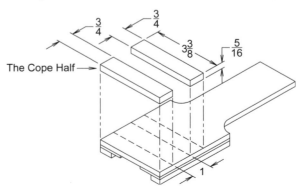

The Cope Half

set in place when the drag is rolled over, and a 1¼" sprue pin is set about 1" away on both sides of the wide portion of the pattern. One serves as a sprue, and the other is a riser.

Make sure your melt is hot enough, or the metal will not fill the shank portion before it freezes.

The slides are fit in the same manner as the spindle head slides, but the clamps are fastened with ¼-20 x ¾" flat head screws instead of the ⁵⁄₁₆" cap screws. Again, fit the clamps with shims so you can take up for wear after use.

Drill the clamp screw holes right through the casting, and countersink the screw heads even with the surface of the clamps.

Install a ¼" x ⅛" x 4" gib with three #10-24 gib screws with jamb nuts.

Two 3⅜" lengths of ¼" x 1" cold rolled steel are fastened to the top pads with ¼-20 x ¾" flat head screws to form the "T" slot for the tool post. File the top pads flat and parallel, and space the screws so that they miss the ones that fasten the clamps.

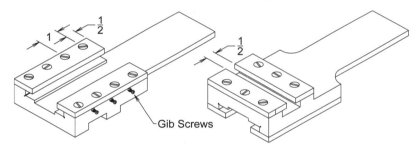

Gib Screws

The clamp screws are spaced ½" from each end, and 1" apart. Center them in the clamp pads.

The gib screws are spaced between the clamp screws.

The screw support differs from that for the spindle head only in dimensions. It is finished and fit in the same way, and the 5½" screw is installed to complete the compound.

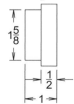

THE TOOL POST

This is an easy between centers lathe job. Just mount a length of 1" stock between centers and machine it to shape and size. Make a starting cut about half way through with a hack saw, but don't attempt to cut all the way through as the work spins. Be very careful of the spinning clamp dog as you make the starting cut.

Locate the center of the post and step drill a row of ⁵⁄₁₆" holes to form the slot. Finish the slot to a smooth fit for a ⅜" square lathe tool by careful hand filing.

Drill and tap a ⁵⁄₁₆-18 hole in the end of the post for the set screw.

Clamp the blank in the vise and finish cutting off with the hack saw.

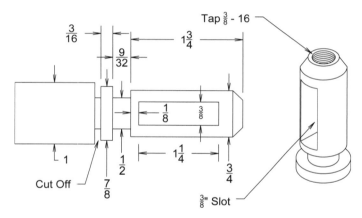

A standard ¾" steel set screw collar can be mounted on the stepped arbor to machine a concave on one surface for the tool post washer, and the rocker can be ground from a 1½" length of ⅜" square key stock.

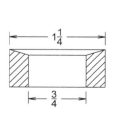

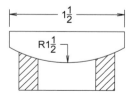

THE SPINDLE NOSE CHUCK

With the compound slide and the tool post complete, the first order of work is to bore the spindle nose chuck.

Make a pair of "V" blocks to support a ¼" boring bar in the tool post. You can make a shallow hack saw cut along the length of the half blocks, and when they are clamped together the cuts will act as a pilot as you step drill to about ³⁄₁₆". Then you can file each half hole to a "V".

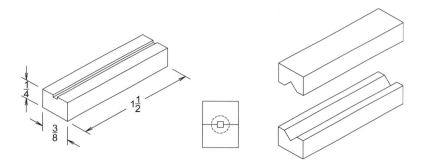

Mount the compound on the temporary work table and fit the tool post with a ¼" forged boring tool in the "V" blocks.

Carefully enlarge the spindle bore to exactly ⅝" to a depth of 1¼". Feed the tool with the carriage screw so that the bore will be exactly parallel to the bed ways. If you attempt to feed with the compound screw the bore will be tapered.

Install two ⁵⁄₁₆" set screws in the spindle nose to complete the spindle nose chuck.

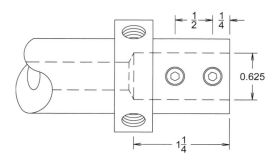

Now you have a miller with a broad range of capabilities that are not usually found on small machines.

The simple set screw chuck is very accurate and effective if it is carefully bored. It will hold all cutters with a ⅝" straight shank, and it can easily be fit with bushings to accept cutters with smaller shanks.

The compound slide makes it possible to bore a spindle with a tapered socket, and when the tail stand is complete you can do taper turning to produce cutter blanks with tapered shanks.

You can cast a face plate of a diameter that is small enough to machine on your lathe, bore it to fit the 1" nose of your spindle, and use it to machine a face plate as large as 14" to 16" in diameter. This means that you can do many large surface facing jobs that are beyond the range of most home work shop equipment.

When the universal compound base is used with the quill support you can do radial drilling at any angle, and you can also fit the quill support with an index wheel for simple dividing work.

The developing miller will do much of the remaining work.

CHAPTER X

HOME MADE CUTTERS

There are so many styles of milling cutters that it would require a separate volume to discuss them all. You have the capability to produce just about any of them, but of course you are limited in the type of material and the degree of precision. An industrial supply catalog or a good text will be all the help you really need.

The geometry and metallurgy of commercially made cutters is highly technical, but manufacturers strive to produce a tool that will endure severe service for long periods of time at very high cutting and feed rates. Requirements are not so exacting in the home shop, and we can make cutters of ordinary tool steel very easily and at low cost.

Multi-toothed cutters offer the advantage of speed, but that is not usually a consideration in the home shop. They also require special equipment and skill to grind them, and few of us have either. While you can easily fit a tool post grinder to your lathe or miller, I always discourage it because the abrasive dust is so destructive to the machines.

When all is considered, multi-toothed cutters, with the exception of slitting saws, are really not needed in the home shop. Their advantage of speed is lost on one of a kind jobs, and we don't have the revenue from the sale of products to justify the cost.

Slitting saws and end mills are the least expensive, and it is often possible to pick them up as salvage for little or nothing. One or more missing teeth from a saw will not prevent you from using it effectively, and an end mill can be ground to relieve all but one flute so that it can be used as though it were a fly cutter.

A broken twist drill can be ground to serve as an end mill, and it's an easy matter to mount them in a ⅝" shank to adapt them to the spindle nose chuck.

For such shapes as dovetail slides, "T" slots, and woodruff keys, you can forge the end of a length of drill rod to the desired shape and size, and grind it to a single cutting edge on an ordinary emery wheel. It is done exactly as you would do in preparing a forged boring tool, except that the cutter is chucked in the spindle nose on an adapter instead of being mounted on the tool post.

This is really a small fly cutter, and most of your end mills and special shaped cutters can be made in this way.

Since there is only one cutting tooth, the shank does not have to be precise. You can grind one cutting edge very near perfect by using a magnifying glass as you compare it with an existing standard, but you could hardly grind two or more edges identical without exotic equipment.

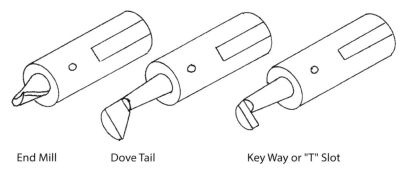

End Mill   Dove Tail   Key Way or "T" Slot

Slitting saws can be mounted on an arbor to fit the spindle nose chuck, and an arbor can be prepared to hold a lathe tool that is ground to a special shape.

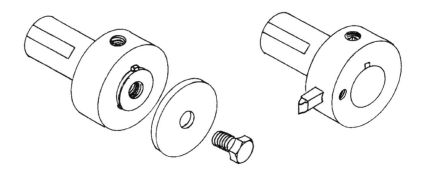

There is a limit to the length of such holders, and some work will be at such distance from the spindle nose that the arbor will need support. The tail stand serves in place of an over arm to support the free end of the arbor. You can prepare an arbor with a square hole at any point, just like the boring bar that was used to bore the spindle. It can be fit with a fly cutter that is ground to any shape to cut splines, keyways, gear teeth, etc.. A hub made of a set screw collar like the one pictured on page 134 can be positioned at any point along the arbor.

Slitting saws need rigid support, and you can fit the arbor with collars to support the saw. It is difficult to cut true screw threads without screw cutting gear, so a jamb collar is the more practical approach for the limited shop.

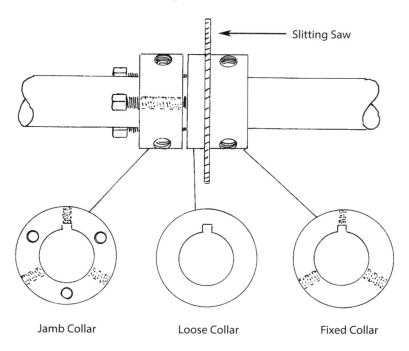

Slitting Saw

Jamb Collar   Loose Collar   Fixed Collar

Standard set screw collars have just one set screw, so two more should be added at 120 degree intervals to the jamb collar and the fixed collar. The jamb collar is tapped for three set screws in line with the bore. The key ways are cut to match the keyway in the saw. If the bore of the saw is larger than ⅝" a shoulder can be machined on the fixed collar, and a pin can be installed as a key. The fixed collar is faced off on the clamping side so the saw will run at right angles to the spindle axis. The set screws in the jamb collar will drive the loose collar against the saw.

AN ADJUSTABLE FACE MILL

The most expensive cutters of all are face mills, and the first job that comes up is a face milling job.

This simple face mill is adjustable from 2¼" to about 4½". Its steel arbor is cast on, and the cutter slot is formed by a steel core. It's an easy casting job, and it requires very little work to finish it. The ¼" lathe bit was my only expense, and it's a very effective tool.

It's a split pattern, and the center line is the only detail that is of particular importance. Note that the slot for the tool bit has one side on the center line. This is a right hand cutter. The slot position would be reversed for a left hand cutter.

THE COPE HALF PATTERN

Glue together two 2½" discs of ¾" stock, and turn them to 2¼" diameter on the lathe.

Saw off the top portion diagonally, and cut the groove and the step with a saw.

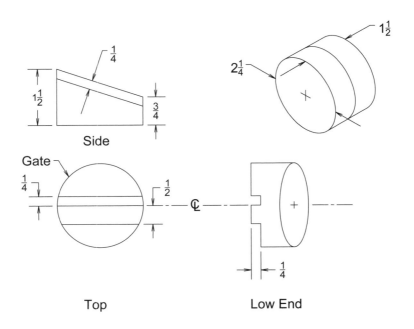

Side

Top

Low End

The position of the slot puts the cutting edge on the center of the turning axis.

A ¼" x ½" x 3½" cold rolled steel core will be molded with the pattern, and it will remain in the mold when the pattern is withdrawn. The core should fit the slot well so that it will form a true slot in the casting, but it must fit freely enough so that it will be left in the mold without damaging the cavity when the pattern is drawn. I wrapped a piece of waxed paper

around the core, lined the slot with body putty, and pressed the core into the slot. The single thickness of waxed paper makes the slot just about right.

THE DRAG HALF PATTERN

The drag half forms the mold for the hub, and it leaves a print for the steel shank which is cast with the holder. It will be best to make it in the lathe so the base of the hub will set the print at right angles to the base of the holder. A small alignment pin is installed to register in the hole in the center of the base of the holder.

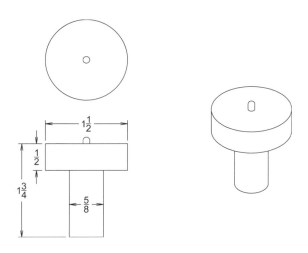

Fit the alignment pin smoothly to the hole in the center of the base, and sand both halves very smooth. Only a very slight amount of draft is needed on the cope half, and none is needed on the drag half.

THE STEEL SHANK

A 2½" length of ⅝" cold rolled steel makes the shank. It is not likely that it would ever turn loose, but I ground a couple of grooves in mine just to be sure.

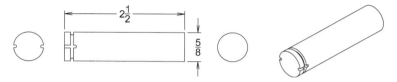

MOLDING THE CUTTER HOLDER

The steel core for the slot will be imbedded in the cope sand so it can't fall out, but the shank is not supported so it must be in the drag.

Drill a small hole in the molding board for the alignment pin, and hold the drag half securely as you ram it up. Rub in the bottom board and roll over the drag.

Set the cope half of the pattern in place, and set the steel core in the slot so that it overhangs equally on both ends.

Set a 1¼" sprue pin about 1" away from the heaviest part of the pattern, but not too close to the steel core.

Ram up the cope, being sure to surround the core, and bed all parts uniformly and securely.

Vent the cope generously, finish the sprue opening, remove the sprue pin, and rub in a bottom board.

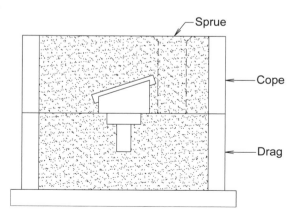

138　　　　*Metal Shop From Scrap Book 4*

Open the mold and lay the cope down to rap and draw the pattern. Rap carefully, so you don't dislodge the steel core. Cut the gate from the cavity to the sprue in the cope rather than in the drag.

Rap and draw the drag pattern, and set the steel shank in its print with the grooved end up. It should extend ¾" above the surface of the drag.

Clean up carefully before you close up, and turn the cope horizontal before you swing it over the drag. If the cope is going to drop out, it will save frustration if you can at least salvage the drag half of the mold.

The melt needs to be a bit hotter than usual because of the chilling effect of the steel members. The sprue size is very important, and the gate must be ample to fill the mold rapidly. If you reduce the size of the sprue to 1", you will probably have a serious shrink flaw in the casting.

FINISHING THE FACE MILL

When the casting has cooled, saw off the gate and clean up as usual. Put a drop of oil on the slot core and support the heavy side of the body in the vise as you strike the end of the core to drive it side ways. One or two blows will loosen it, and then it will be easy to knock it out. A bit of hand filing will be needed to bring the groove to a good fit for a ¼" lathe tool bit.

Grind a flat on the shank, and mount it in the spindle nose chuck to machine the outside diameter true.

Carefully drill and tap for four #6-32 set screws to bear against the side of the cutting tool.

Grind the tool with slight side rake and top relief, and relieve the end for clearance on the cutting circle.

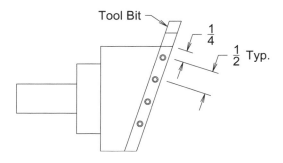

CHAPTER XI
THE PERMANENT WORK TABLE

The temporary work table will certainly not be as true as would be required for some classes of work. It is likely to have an error in the alignment of the "T" slot, and its top surface will not be true flat.

It is adequate for milling the casting for the permanent table, but steps must be taken to avoid repeating its errors.

The procedure is simple. We fit the table with a right angle plate and mill its surface true flat. The permanent work table is then bolted to the angle plate and both surfaces are milled parallel. The accuracy of the operation is dependent only on the trueness of the edges of the temporary work table slide.

Milling the right angle plate also gives you an opportunity to perfect the alignment of the cross feed, for the face mill will make a concave cut in one direction of feed if the cross feed is not at exact right angles to the bed. A bit of scraping in the vertical pads of the box ways will correct any error.

You will begin to appreciate the versatility of the design as you perform operations that you may have thought required a vertical milling machine.

THE ANGLE PLATE PATTERN

The right angle plate will serve to mill the casting for the permanent work table, and it will be a valuable accessory for future jobs as well.

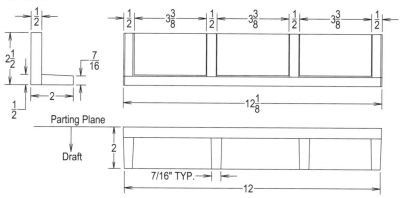

The basic section thickness is ½" throughout the pattern, but note that the triangular members taper from ½" to ⁷⁄₁₆". Also note that the pattern measures 12⅛" at the parting plane, and tapers to 12". The narrow leg of the angle also tapers from ½" to ⁷⁄₁₆".

This pattern is similar in nature to the one for the head stand. The outside angle at the junction is 90 degrees, but the inside angles are all slightly more than 90 degrees so that the pattern will be well drafted. Assemble the members carefully so that it will be easy to draw from the mold.

Wipe a small fillet on all inside corners, and round the outside corners except at the parting plane.

Ram the pattern into the drag, and vent very generously before you roll over the drag. Steam and gas will collect at the inside corners to cause serious flaws if the mold is not well vented. Rub in the bottom board and roll over the drag.

Set a 1¼" sprue pin about 1" away from the outside corner in the center of the pattern, and ram up and vent the cope.

The pattern will draw very easily if it is properly drafted. If the cavity breaks up when you attempt to draw, correct the error in the pattern.

Clean up the cavity very carefully before you close up to pour. You don't want sand inclusions in this casting.

MILLING THE ANGLE PLATE

The temporary work table will not be perfectly true, so a pair of ¾" or 1" set screw collars are used as spacers so that the error of the table won't be transferred to the angle plate.

Step drill two ⅜" holes on 8" centers on the center line of both legs of the angle plate. Use ⁵⁄₁₆" "T" nuts and bolts to fasten the angle plate to the temporary work table.

The wide leg is milled first so that the narrow leg can be left in position for milling the work table casting.

These operations use the extreme limit of cross travel, so the angle plate must be positioned to the rear of the work table so that the cutter will clear at the beginning of the cut.

Align the angle plate so that its surface travels parallel to the line of cross travel.

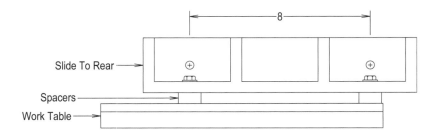

Set the diameter of the face mill to about 2¾", and adjust the height of the spindle head to center the mill on the angle plate. Tighten the clamp bolt on the vertical slide, and make sure all gibs are snug. Set the spindle speed for 270 RPM, which is the highest speed in the low range.

Make a light cut in both directions of travel to evaluate the alignment of the carriage. The tool should cut only on the leading half of the revolution, though it will carry a chip around to make a circular scratch on the milled surface from time to time when it is near perfect.

Both legs will be milled again when the angle is fit to the permanent table, so mill it only enough to provide a true surface for milling the table casting.

Mill the wide leg first, then remount the angle with the same spacers and mill the narrow leg. When the second leg is milled it must be left in the same mounting position until both sides of the permanent work table casting have been milled parallel.

THE PERMANENT TABLE CASTING

This is a very simple pattern. Only minimum draft is required, and it's fed with a 1¼" sprue about 1" away on either side near the center.

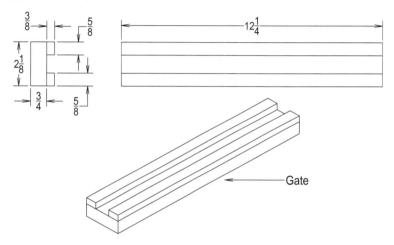

Gate

MILLING THE PERMANENT TABLE CASTING

Step drill and tap two ⁵⁄₁₆-18 holes in the center of the casting to match the ⅜" holes in the angle plate.

File the divided top surface until it will rest on the angle plate without wobble, then bolt it to the angle and mill the base first. Then invert it on the angle and mill the top surface parallel to the base surface.

Take plenty of time with your set up, and use these first operations to familiarize yourself with the machine and to correct any imperfections in it.

Check the fit of the spindle bearings frequently, and remove shims to adjust the fit when it becomes neccessary. Early wear will be rapid, but the bearings will give long service when they have worn to fit the spindle.

Check the slide gibs too, and make adjustment as it is needed.

The set screw collars that provide thrust bearing for the spindle may need adjustment, and the feed screw collars may need to be snugged up. Oil all bearings well.

ASSEMBLE THE PERMANENT WORK TABLE

While you could use the ¼" x 3" slide from the temporary table, it would be very difficult to use the existing bolt holes in any of the members. It will be better to use the temporary table as an auxilliary for the miller and shaper, and use new material to build the permanent table.

Take extra care to assemble the parts parallel to the slide, and note that more screws are used for the permanent table than were used on the temporary table.

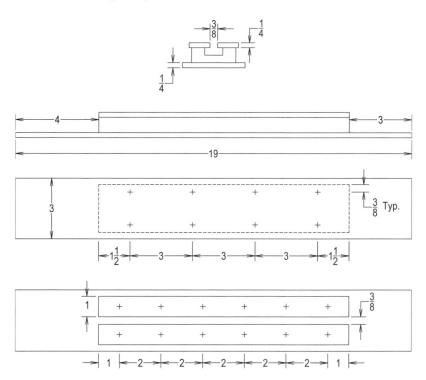

All assembly is with ¼-20 x ¾" flat head screws, as were used for the temporary table. Clamp securely and step drill as for all stacked assemblies. Bolt the casting to the slide first, then install the right hand top rail only.

Transfer the screw support assembly from the temporary work

table, and install the permanent slide in the carriage cross slide. Align the screw support carefully before you tap the holes in the slide to screw it in place.

Adjust up the gibs in the slide, and set the cutter to make a very light cut along the left side of the right hand rail. This will establish the "T" slot in exact alignment with the normal cutting line. The left hand top rail is installed with a ⅜" wide spacer between, and both edges of the left hand rail will be a true reference point for set up on all future jobs.

FIT THE ANGLE PLATE TO THE PERMANENT TABLE

A 7" length of ³⁄₁₆" x ⅜" key stock is screwed to the angle plate between the mounting holes so that it will return to its original position each time it is used. Then it is installed on the permanent work table to mill it true flat. Install the key with ³⁄₁₆" flat head screws, and put in a pair of dowel pins so it can't slip.

This will equip you for all types of work that would be done on a vertical mill, and it expands the limit of cross travel because you can mill a portion of the length, then slide the angle plate to finish a longer than usual job.

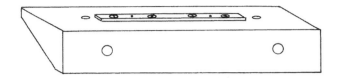

FIT THE UNIVERSAL BASE TO THE PERMANENT TABLE

You should install a key on the universal base so that you can fasten the divided scale to it for easy set up. An adjustable witness mark plate on each of your swivel bases will enable you to calibrate each one to the base.

DESIGN YOUR OWN ACCESSORIES

Now you have the means to fit your shop out with just about any type of accessory you might need. A swivel base vise, dividing fixtures, angle plates and adjustable angle plates. They are all possible now, and you have only begun to build your shop.

CHAPTER XII

THE TAIL STAND

The main objection to a vertical mill is that there is not enough support for the cutter when work must be done at some distance from the spindle nose.

This machine has all the versatility of a vertical mill for such jobs as slotting, sinking, profiling, etc., and it also has the rigidity of a horizontal mill when the tail stand is used to support the free end of the arbor for large work.

The tail stand clamps to the bed ways like the lathe tail stock, and its vertical screw is the same pitch as the head stand. It has a simple bronze bushing in a sliding boss, so it can be aligned with the spindle even if you have made an error in erecting the vertical slide of either member.

It's a much easier job than the head stand because you have the miller to do most of the work for you.

THE BASE PATTERN

A simple pattern, needing only minimum draft. Feed it with a 1¼" sprue at either side, and a riser at the opposite side.

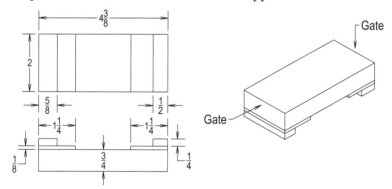

FITTING THE BASE

If you have the metal shaper this is a simple job. If not, the box slide can be fitted by hand scraping. The top surface and the clamp pads can be faced off on the lathe.

There will be two ⁵⁄₁₆-18 tapped holes in the top, and these should be drilled with the base and stand clamped together. It will be best to do any machining operations after these holes have been drilled and tapped.

The base fits the bed ways in the same way as the carriage, but it is not meant to slide along the ways. It has no gib, but a screw is used to draw the front box against the front edge of the ways to align it.

The front clamp is ⅛" x ¾" x 2" steel, fastened with two ¼-20 x ¾" flat head screws. This is so it will clear the carriage screw support when it is used at the end of the bed ways. Shims are used to bring the box ways to a close fit on the bed ways.

The back clamp is ¼" x 1" x 2" steel, and it is locked with two ⁵⁄₁₆-18 x 1½" cap screws that tighten from the top.

Notice that the clamping bolts are partly in the gib space like the clamp bolt on the spindle head. They should just clear the bed ways.

The back clamp is removed and the gib screw is backed out to install the base on the bed. Then the gib screw is drawn snug to align the base before the clamp screws are tightened.

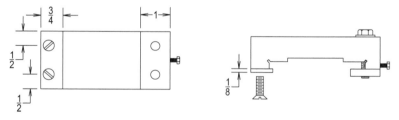

THE TAIL STAND PATTERN

The broad flat surface of segment #1 is the parting plane. Its section thickness is ½", but all other segments taper from ½" to ⁷⁄₁₆" section thickness for draft.

Draft is the all important consideration in this pattern, because there is so much vertical surface to bind it in the mold.

We have the miller to plane the vital surfaces now, so we don't have to be careful of the outside angle as we did for the head stand casting.

The cope half of the pattern is a simple rectangle that forms the pad for the ways. It's aligned with two pins, and a small fillet is wiped on to adhere to the cope half.

It's a routine split pattern mold, but the heavy pad requires a riser to avoid a shrink flaw. Feed it with a 1¼" sprue at the base, and a 1¼" riser at the opposite end. Set both pins about 1" away. Vent both the cope and drag generously with the wire.

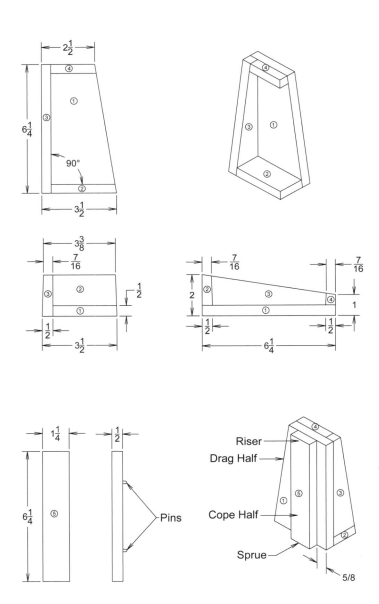

MACHINING THE TAIL STAND

The milling machine can do all of the needed work on the head stand. Your filing and hand scraping days are about over now, but you won't regret the effort you've spent.

Drill a ⅜" hole through the center of the pad, about 1½" above the base. Align the pad with the left edge of the work table with a square, and bolt it to the table with one ⁵⁄₁₆" bolt through the "T" slot.

Mill the base of the casting with the face mill.

The tail stand is fastened to the base with two ⁵⁄₁₆" x 1" cap screws. The holes will have to be step drilled through the bottom of the base with the members clamped together, so the clamps will have to be removed for the drilling operation.

Locate the bolt centers so that the heads will clear the vertical ribs of the head stand. One of the bolt holes will pass through the front wear pad on the base, but that won't cause any problem.

Step drill both holes through to tap size, enlarge the holes in the head stand to ⁵⁄₁₆", and tap the holes in the base. Assemble with bolts, washers, and lock washers.

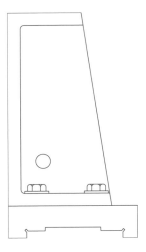

Re-install the clamps and position the assembly on the bed to mill the vertical pad. The head stand screw is not intended as a feed screw, but it will serve for this job because we want the tail stand pad to be parallel to the vertical travel of the spindle head. Position the assembly so that the face mill will make a cut of about .050". Be careful not to damage the ways with the gib screw.

INSTALL THE TAIL STAND WAYS

A slab of ¼" x 2" x 8" cold rolled is fastened to the pad with six ¼-20 x ¾" flat head screws. Test the surface of the pad after milling, and hand scrape to true flat if neccessary.

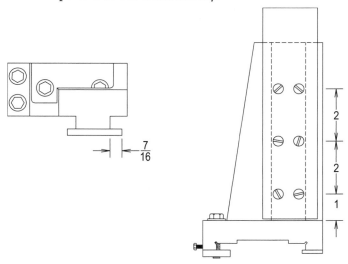

Make every effort to install the ways exactly vertical, but an error is not critical because of the horizontal adjustment of the bearing boss.

THE TAIL STAND SLIDE COPE PATTERN

The drag half of this pattern is the same one you made for the compound slide. The new cope half is a simple rectangle that replaces the compounds twin pads.

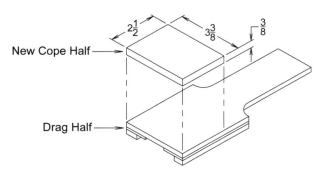

Molding of the tail stand slide is the same as for the compound slide, and so is the fitting of the clamps and the gib.

THE TAIL STAND SCREW SUPPORT

Like the compound slide screw support, but the center of the screw is farther from the shank of the slide.

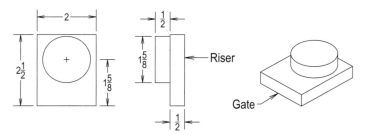

Molding, machining, and installation of the screw support are the same as for the compound. Install the 6" screw with its washers and the hand wheel. The screw threads into the top webb of the tail stand. There is no screw tunnel, so you must locate the center carefully so the screw will clear the vertical portion of the casting. The bushing and special center punch will locate the tap hole center.

THE TAIL STAND BEARING BOSS PATTERN

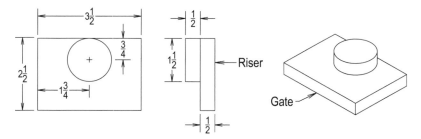

The bearing boss is molded and machined just like the screw supports. It's fit with a ¾" x ⅝" bushing, and a set screw is installed in the hub so that it can be mounted on an arbor for facing off.

The slide is installed on the stand, and the stand is installed on the bed in position to mill the face of the slide. The tail stand screw is used to feed the slide vertically, so the pad will be milled parallel to the slide ways.

A 3⅜" length of ¼" x 1" steel is screwed to the pad with two ¼-20 x ¾" flat head screws, and the boss is fastened to the slide with a ⁵⁄₁₆" x 1¼" cap screw through the ⅜" x 2⅜" elongated hole in the boss flange.

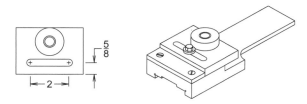

The elongated hole in the boss permits aligning the tail stand center with the head spindle so that you can set the arbor parallel to the bed even if there is an error in the vertical travel of either slide.

You can install cone centers in both the spindle nose and the tail stand, and you have a generous set-over for between centers taper turning.

CONCLUSION

Your milling machine is finished now, but that's not the end. There will be errors that need correcting, and you may even do some of your work over. It will be easier now that you have the milling machine to do some of the work.

If you have followed the series in sequence you have retraced the steps of some of the early pioneers in the machine tool industry. You can see the great potential of these simple methods, and the latent ability in your hands and your mind. It requires only determination, and you can develop a high level of skill by simple exercise. You don't need a teacher, just tackle the job and criticise the results. You will be pleased and amazed at what you can do.

Like all of the machines in the series, the miller is presented in its most fundamental form. You have the essential elements, and this gives you the means to build an even better machine. It will be easy to build a larger miller, and you can design with ball bearing spindle, much heavier members, and you can even make gears for a back geared spindle head. Basic accessories are not difficult to design if you do it with aluminum castings. You can even make a very accurate dividing plate by fitting the spindle with a gear or sprocket.

Just mount it on the outboard end of the spindle, add a plunger to lock it on each tooth, and drill holes in the plate with the quill. Mount the dividing plate on the quill support with a plunger, and you have a simple dividing fixture for the work table.

The universal base makes it possible to set up for many compound motions, and there is hardly a milling operation that you can't perform if you give it a bit of study.

I spent a great deal of time in trying to workout a simple power feed for the work table, but had to give up in despair. When this type of machine was in common use, they had an automatic feed, and it was called the drop mechanism. You will see the mechanism on some of the engravings early in the manual. It was a worm wheel that was driven by the worm on a separate shaft. There were stops on the work table that operated a lever that caused the worm shaft to drop out of mesh at the end of a cut. The stops were adjustable in a "T" slot in the side of the work table, so a cut of any length within the capacity of the machine could be preset. They may not have termed it so then, but that was automation. I've noticed that some of the small hobby shop type of millers offer a separate electric motor drive for a power feed that looks a lot like the rotissery drive on my outdoor barbeque grill. It would not be very practical to vary the speed, but such a drive may be practical within some limits.

Metal working is a great hobby for relaxation and profit, and we never stop the learning process. Problems that were impossible to solve a month ago are duck soup today. Don't be intimidated by any project, just dig in and amaze yourself. You'll be glad you did it.

INDEX

The "Build Your Own Metal Working Shop From Scrap" Series: